I'd Like to Run Wild!
A Wellness Action Guide

Written by
Jean Steel

Illustrated by Suz Roehl

Run wild!
♡ Jean

This book is dedicated to my dad, Horton Walker Steel, who modeled for us all the philosophy of "life is short" and "go for it." Wish you could be here in person, but your spirit is and for that I am grateful.

ISBN 13: 978-0-615-15826-6

Library of Congress Control Number: 2007937436

Introduction

This is not a sit-down-and-read-it-all-at-once kind of book. Heck, you don't even have to read the chapters in order! Just as we are all works-in-progress, this book began that way too, as a loose compilation of my most requested keynote talks. Over time it has evolved into the most complete array of Wellness factoids, methods, stats, and studies I could assemble. Personal stories, plus those from family and clients bring humor and pathos into the mix, leaving you with a volume designed to be used as a "travel" guide on your journey to wellness.

We've all had them: those seemingly inconsequential encounters that end up changing the course of our lives. In retrospect (of course!), here's the one that shaped my career, this book, my life!

I was teaching at a home health care agency one day when a nurse named Donna asked me if I had a minute. She wanted to show me something. But before she handed me the scrap of paper with a spidery scrawl of words on it, she told me about the woman who'd written them. She was in her late 80's, Donna told me, and had suffered a stroke that left her bedridden and unable to speak. Her prognosis was not favorable.

Copyright 2004 by Randy Glasbergen. www.glasbergen.com

—GLASBERGEN—

"In one way or another, we're all confined by invisible fencing."

When a male nurse went to visit the woman, he asked a simple question on a piece of paper that read, "How do you feel?" He then handed the paper and pen to this woman for her response. The note I now held in my hand said "I'd like to run wild." Not I wish I could walk or talk, but "I'd like to run wild!" I was deeply moved. Most of us have the capacity to run wild, but how many of us do it? Are we too mature, too sophisticated? Too busy? What's holding us back?

I knew this would be the title of my book and I knew I needed to sit down and write it. When I finished it, I ran wild.

I run wild every chance I get.

What does that mean for you? Can I get you to run wild with me?

Chapter 1

My Wellness Epiphany
Why Listen to Me?

Life is short ... No, it isn't! When you think about it, it's the longest thing you'll ever do.
~ from *Stupid and Contagious* by Caprice Crane

Years before the mind-body connection was a popular concept, I met a man who inspired the new direction my career would take. In fact, this guy—let's call him David—is the catalyst for the book you hold in your hands.

I was working as a health educator in a large hospital, designing a preventative health course for our HMO clients. The course was pretty basic and consisted of things like what screenings to get at what age, fundamental nutrition, and the importance of exercise—all based on the commonly held view of health at the time: that health is the absence of disease.

During the session, David volunteered information about his health that baffled him. He was not yet 50, and for the past two years he'd begun to suffer from high blood pressure, heart problems, and migraines. He claimed that nothing had happened that might contribute to his steadily declining health.

After class, David asked whether I might suggest a therapist from the hospital's psychiatry department. He and his wife had a teenage daughter, he explained, who had broken her neck two years ago and was now paralyzed. David couldn't discuss it; but his wife needed help dealing with it, and thought that talking with a professional might be the right thing to do. Two things alarmed me about this man's tragic story. One, he did not see the connection between his daughter's accident and the physical symptoms he'd described earlier in class. And two, none of his doctors did either! David's symptoms were a textbook example of stress-related illnesses. When I quizzed a number of doctors later, they all said the same thing: "We don't have time to ask about their personal lives when we only have 12 minutes per patient to examine and treat." Real wellness was in real trouble.

Harvard Medical School came to the rescue with a cutting-edge mind/body program. After teaching their courses, I not only became an avid believer, but also created a Masters of Science program in Wellness at Sacramento State University. I took courses in a variety of disciplines, among them: recreation and leisure, sociology, counseling, health, and communication.

Once I graduated, I began offering stress management classes (among others) to businesses, cities, schools, and corporations. The rationale was simple. People who are unusually stressed don't have time to attend a stress reduction course. But they would, if it was offered and paid for by the boss, right? Companies are buying into the Wellness concept because they understand that self-care is critical to their bottom line. Happy, healthy employees are better for business.

Now rewind the clock a few years ... to my first "wellness" moment of clarity.

When I was six years old, I lived in Los Angeles with my parents and three younger sisters. My father had a Master's Degree in herpetology (the study of reptiles and amphibians) and worked as an L.A.

County Sheriff (if that tells you anything about following your passion). One day he brought a gentleman dressed in gauzy, embroidered robes home to dinner. Turns out he was from Ethiopia and he invited us all to visit. My father was fascinated.

Before my seventh birthday had rolled around, we were living in Addis Ababa, Ethiopia – four little blonde girls and their mother, still in shock.

At seven, I had no idea that this was at all unusual. I did not experience culture shock having not experienced enough culture in my young life to notice. As little white blondies, we were oddities, to be sure, but the Ethiopians are loving, kind, beautiful spirits and they treated us wonderfully.

Years later, I learned that my grandparents were terrified for us. So I asked my father what prompted him to move us to Africa. He told me that if we had been miserable, we would have returned home. Life is short, so go for it. That was my role modeling. And it stuck.

Following are some caveats I learned directly from those experiences that continue to serve me well:

1. Wellness is about recognizing that life is short.

> *Enjoy yourself. It's later than you think.*
> ~ Chinese Proverb

> *Most of us spend our lives as if we had
> another one in the bank.*
> ~ Ben Irwin.

My parents eventually returned to the U.S. and built their dream retirement home on the Central Coast of California. Soon after they settled in, my father began to forget things, and he was diagnosed with Alzheimer's. We can be happy and healthy one minute, and get a phone call the next that can change our lives in an instant.

3

I had a student one semester named Ben. Funny guy, great to have in class. One of the last days of the semester he asked me whether he could miss any more classes without affecting his grade. I checked his attendance and told him no. He looked crestfallen. Seems his buddies had asked him to go waterskiing, but the plan conflicted with my class. "If you really practice what you preach, you'd let me go," argued Ben. "Ten years from now, I'll remember that day on the lake with my friends," he continued, "but probably not the day I sat in your class." Ouch! Much as it pained me (how could he forget *my* class?), I told him to go. He got the message: Life is too short.

So, eat dessert first, live each day as if it were your last, and move your family to Africa (if that really lights you up!).

2. Wellness is about taking responsibility.

Man must cease attributing his problems to his environment, and learn again to exercise his will - his personal responsibility.
~ Albert Schweitzer

If you haven't the strength to impose your own terms upon life, you must accept the terms it offers you.
~ T.S. Elliot

I find this notion empowering. If I don't like what life offers me, I can change things. I can choose my reactions, my moods, my dreams. I can choose my own destiny. If you are arguing with me, you haven't tested it. Think about it. To every single thing that happens in our life, we choose how we will react to it, how we'll feel about it later, what we'll do or not do about it. But we resist that responsibility because it's so much easier to blame others for our misfortunes. Here's a great cartoon caption I saw years ago under a drawing of a newscaster delivering the evening news. "We have late breaking news. Someone in the United States just took personal responsibility for their actions. More on this later."

4

3. Wellness is about making choices.

The last of the human freedoms is to
choose one's attitude.
~ *Victor Frank.*

I often see the notion of wellness misused. A program offering "total wellness" isn't "total" at all if it only addresses the physical element. I like the definition of wellness from a textbook I use. It has an expanded definition that says "Wellness is largely determined by the decisions you make about how to live your life." We move in a process toward wellness with every choice, every decision we make, dozens of times a day. I can make the choice (and some days I have to make it 50 times a day!) to be happy, to laugh, to be grateful.

The difficulty in life is the choice.
~ George Moore

My friend Mary (a former student) got a call from her husband Aaron one day complaining of a terrible headache. On his way home from work, he had to pull over and passed out. Mary found him a few hours later and the ER folks discovered he'd had a brain aneurysm burst. Aaron was comatose and in the hospital for several months. Meanwhile Mary was raising their infant daughter on her own. Aaron eventually recovered consciousness but has permanent deficits. Mary cannot leave him at home alone. When I met her, she was taking one college class each week while someone watched Aaron and their daughter. I thought her story was tragic until she showed me a fresh tattoo on her arm. "Blessed" it says. Blessed, for pete's sake, in the face of all that hardship. Mary has chosen to feel blessed when she could just as easily choose to feel beaten. Her choice to feel blessed makes her well, makes her happy, makes her productive... and what she doesn't know is that it makes me feel inspired!

Chapter 2

Jump-Starting Your Own Wellness Epiphany

All I know, is just what I read in the papers.
~ Will Rogers

www.glasbergen.com

"I already diagnosed myself on the Internet.
I'm only here for a second opinion."

At least half of the emails I receive about health are either inaccurate or outright hoaxes. The idea that if it's in print, it must be true is just about as silly as believing that a baby was born with a wooden leg …(Wait, that isn't true, is it?)

Taking good care of yourself means being an informed consumer. The internet is a vast and rich resource for information on everything from curing the common cold to plastic surgery. Do your homework, check your sources, and check the source of your sources. How current is the information? How recently was the site updated?

Use the same diligence and thoroughness when dealing with other sources of information as well: magazines, newspaper articles, radio shows, television info-mercials and the like. Much of this information is simplified or paraphrased. Find the original source. Look for sample size in the study. Were the results published in a reputable journal?

The FDA suggests we follow these guidelines in order to be *safer*:
• Speak up
• Ask questions
• Find the facts
• Evaluate your choices
• Read the label and follow directions

Taking care of yourself also means being an active partner with your doctor or health care practitioner. A physician once scolded me for encouraging my students in an assertiveness training class to ask questions during a doctor's office visit. He said he only had a few minutes with each patient, and did not have time for "chit chat." Find someone who does.

Being an informed consumer means taking responsibility for the information you use and share. It takes some time to do your homework, but thoroughly informed decisions will help you to feel more confident about the real state of your overall health.

Chapter 3

Wellness Wheel

If you are looking for balance, this is the perfect activity. A college professor introduced me to this concept and I found it so useful that I've used it, modified it, and added a battery of questions in order to make it more accurate. In the end, you'll have a colorful visual that will tell you where the real work needs to begin.

So here's the only rule: Look at the questions and answer them honestly BEFORE you pick up the colored pens. The questions are designed to provoke some real honesty so that you can see where the imbalances are. This tool is only as useful as the effort you put into it – like anything in life.

Each spoke represents a different facet of your life. Once you've answered the questions provided, ask yourself: On a scale of one to ten, how satisfied are you with these various facets of life?

The 10 spokes of the wheel represent BALANCE. Seeing the center of the wheel as zero, and with ten being a full spoke, fill in each one in with a different color. Here is a sample of how the finished product might look:

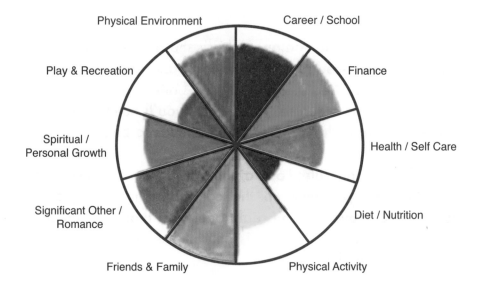

This person has a 10 in "Friends & Family;" a 3 in "Diet & Nutrition"; and a 7 or 8 in "Spiritual & Personal Growth."

Once you complete the activity, ask yourself: How smoothly does my wheel turn? How bumpy would my life be if this were a real wheel? What does this tell me? Use this as a guide to help you set goals and priorities for bringing wellness and balance into your life.

So grab some colored marking pens, and let's get started. At the end of the questions section, I've given you your very own wheel to color in. (No scoffing allowed. It's fun, it's easy and it's oh-so-revealing!).

QUESTIONS FOR YOUR WELLNESS WHEEL

This is in no way a complete list. Use it to jump-start the evaluation process; ignore the questions that are not relevant, and add your own!

CAREER/SCHOOL

- Is your career/major your passion?
- Does time fly by when you are at work/school?
- Do you look forward to work?
- Do you feel like you are making a difference?
- Do you have good friends at work/school?
- Does your work offer personal and professional development?
- Is/are your work/classes personally rewarding?
- Is your work financially rewarding?
- Do you get along well with co-workers/classmates?
- Do you feel you work well as a team?
- Do you get along well with your manager/professors?
- Do you believe in the mission of your workplace?
- Is the mission of your work in sync with personal values?

FINANCE

- Do you have a stable source of income?
- Do you have 6 months living expenses in an available account?
- Do you live within your means?
- Do you balance your bank statement every month?
- Do you pay bills on time?
- Do you live debt free or utilize a plan to get there?
- Do you consistently contribute to a savings plan?
- Do you dream about winning the lottery or other gimmicks to fund your future?
- Do you know where your money goes and how much is spent on personal and/or business expenses?
- Do you have a long term financial plan that supports your present and future goals?
- Do you have an excellent financial planner/accountant?
- Do you have a bookkeeping system that allows you to access your financial information at any moment?

HEALTH/SELF CARE

- Do you wear your seat belt at all times?
- Do you understand the health care system and use it intelligently?
- Do you drink and drive?
- Do you recognize your health is your responsibility?
- Do you know how to manage your stress?
- Do you floss daily?
- Do you have regular dental check-ups?
- Do you know your cholesterol level? Is it under 200?
- Do you know your blood pressure?
- Are you hypertensive? Are you doing something about it?
- Do you get 7-8 hours of sleep every night?
- Do you have a strong immune system – able to avoid most infectious diseases?
- Women – Do you examine your breasts monthly? Do you get regular mammograms?
- Do you have lots of energy? Enough to get you through the day without getting tired half way through it?
- Do you get the screenings you need to?
- Are your immunizations up to date?
- Do you listen to your body? When it talks to you, do you take the steps to fix what's wrong?
- Do you smoke?
- Do you know your family health history?
- Do you know the facts about the common causes of death in the US? And do you use that knowledge to protect yourself as best you can?
- Do you use recreational drugs?

DIET
- Do you read the labels on foods? Do you know what you are looking for?
- Do you eat according to the new food pyramid?
- Do you maintain a desirable weight?
- Do you drink enough water?
- Do you drink a lot of sugary soda?
- Do you get enough calcium?
- Do you drink too much caffeine?
- Do you eat fish?
- Do you eat high fiber foods?
- Do you eat a lot of salt? processed foods?
- Do you drink whole milk?
- Do you eat a lot of saturated fat?
- Do you take a multivitamin?

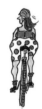

EXERCISE
- Do you engage in vigorous exercise (cardio) at least 3X a week?
- Do you exercise to strengthen muscles and joints?
- Do you feel good about the condition of your body?
- Do you warm up before exercise? Cool down afterward?
- Do you take the stairs when you can?
- Do you walk when you can, rather than drive?
- Do you use appropriate gear?

FRIENDS & FAMILY
- Have you told your parents/children recently that you love them?
- Do you get along well with siblings?
- Do you interact with others in a healthy way?
- Have you let go of relationships that drag you down?
- Do you spend quality time with family?
- Do you have friends/family who love you for who you are, not what you do for them?
- Do you dread running into anyone?
- Do you feel good about the impression you make on people?
- Are you open, honest and get along well with others?
- Do you enjoy being with those who are different from you?

SIGNIFICANT OTHER

- Are you open to a loving and responsible relationship?
- Are they your best friend or soul mate?
- Are they someone you can talk to about private feelings?
- Do they try to change you to what they want?
- Are they faithful?
- Are you satisfied with your sex life?
- Do you engage in activities together and apart?
- Does jealousy get in the way of a happy relationship?
- Do you engage in healthy communication?
- Do you feel listened to?
- Do you share the work of maintaining the house?

SPIRITUAL/PERSONAL GROWTH

- Do you believe your life is a precious gift?
- Do you take time to enjoy beauty and nature? Is your life rewarding?
- Do you participate in life-long learning?
- Do you have high self-esteem?
- Do you have something to look forward to every day?
- Do you live life according to your values?
- Do you express your creativity?
- Do you engage in acts of caring without asking for anything in return?
- Do you touch others in a positive way?
- Are you content with who you are?
- Do you have goals, and have a plan to achieve them?
- Do you live in the here-and-now, rather than past and future?
- Do you engage in some sort of self-reflection daily? Take time alone?

PLAY & RECREATION

- Are you satisfied with your outlets for play?
- Do you watch too much TV?
- Do you get bored?
- Do you give yourself permission to do nothing? To relax?
- Do you do activities you love on a consistent basis?
- Do you maintain regular participation in a hobby or craft?
- Do you participate in a wide variety of social activities?
- Are you broadening your leisure activities as you get older?
- Are there things you love to do, but just can't find the time?
- Do you enjoy your leisure activities for the relaxation they provide?
- Do you get just as much pleasure in planning and anticipating a leisure experience, as you do in participating in the actual activity itself?
- Do you enjoy reflecting and looking back on the good times you had?

PHYSICAL ENVIRONMENT

- Do you look forward to coming home to your personal oasis?
- Is your home neat and clean?
- Is your home full of clutter?
- Do you live in a place you love? The city? Your home?
- Does your bedroom let you have the best sleep possible?
- Is your car clean and in good condition?
- Are your plants and animals thriving?
- Do you surround yourself with beautiful things?
- Is your home organized? Your desk/work area?
- Do you understand how your environment affects your health?
- Have you taken the right actions to improve it?

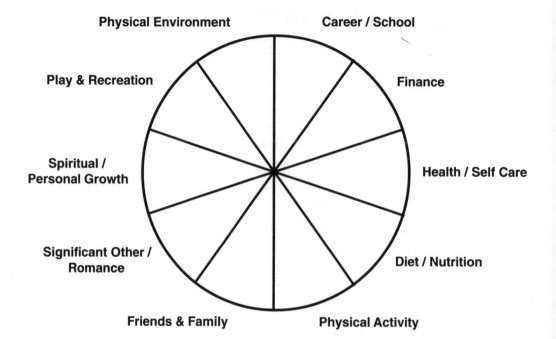

Physical Environment

Career / School

Play & Recreation

Finance

Spiritual /
Personal Growth

Health / Self Care

Significant Other /
Romance

Diet / Nutrition

Friends & Family

Physical Activity

Chapter 4

Creating A Plan -
Making A Change

The message I get most often from participants whenever I teach a class goes something like this: "You got me so motivated. Thank you!" I believe them, I really do. But tomorrow, when the alarm goes off and they stumble over the family cat on their way to the coffee pot, I wonder how many of them will really make the changes they hope for.

There is a saying: "The only person who likes change is a wet baby." So if you don't have a specific plan for it, you'll curse at the cat, pour the coffee you swore you wouldn't drink today into a travel cup, and go back to the same old way you've always done things. Motivation dies without a plan of action.

"I'm afraid you caught me at a bad time...
somewhere between college and retirement!"

You're ready. I know you are! That's why you bought this book for pete's sake. And guess what? This chapter is the "plan" that will keep your motivation alive and kicking. Starting here, starting now. So, why now? Here are some of the answers I've heard. Maybe one of them will resonate with you.

- I wandered into the kitchen at a social gathering and over-heard this: "Here comes the party queen. Hide the booze!"
- I was shopping with my pregnant friend for maternity clothes for *her* and the saleswoman thought *I* was the pregnant one.
- My doctor suggested I stop smoking, lose weight, eat better, get more exercise and sleep.
- I turned 30 (or 40, or 50, or 60).
- I picked up my new passport photo and didn't recognize myself.
- I got divorced (or married, or my children moved out, or my parents died).
- I was told I would die sooner than later unless I... Fill in the blank
- I read an article that explained the long term effects of unchecked diabetes.
- I heard a news report on the link between _____ and cancer.
- I am just sick and tired of feeling sick and tired.
- The real truth is

_____

_____

_____

_____

The first thing to do (don't you just love *first* things?) is to ask yourself the following questions:

Is this goal realistic?
As the wellness coordinator for MCI/WORLDCOM, I taught their Weight Loss/Management classes. I would meet individually with each participant prior to the class to determine their readiness. "How much would you like to lose and why?" I would ask. To which many would answer "Thirty pounds by my high school reunion two months

from now." Now, I am all for optimism, but the goal of winning the lottery to pay your bills or moving to New York at 40 to become a super model...well, let's just say...can you try to be realistic?

<u>Is this a good time for me to pursue it?</u>
Are you ready to make a change? What or who would support you? Work against you? What are the pros and cons of this change? Is it right before the holidays? Is it when you have split from a partner? When you lost your job? Often a catalyst that motivates change is a good time, but it can also set you up for failure. Upsets and challenges can zap your energy. Don't add a major change until you have recovered.

PROS OF CHANGE	CONS OF CHANGE
_____	_____
_____	_____
_____	_____
_____	_____
_____	_____
_____	_____
_____	_____

Here's an example: Let's say you want to learn to be more assertive with your in-laws. The pros could include reduced stress, improved self-esteem, reduced anxiety when they come to visit, increased self-respect, and feeling like an equal in the relationship. The cons? Your in-laws could get angry or confused. They might decide to stop talking to you. Increased tension among you, your spouse, and them. You might be misunderstood. Your spouse might get defensive.

QUESTIONS:
WHAT ARE YOU AFRAID OF?

_____

_____

_____

_____

_____

WHAT IS THE WORST THING THAT COULD HAPPEN IF YOU ACHIEVE THIS GOAL?

_____

_____

_____

_____

WHAT ARE THE REALISTIC CHANCES OF THIS HAPPENING?

_____

_____

_____

_____

WHAT IS THE BEST THING THAT COULD HAPPEN IF YOU ACHIEVE THIS GOAL?

_____

_____

_____

_____

REMEMBER - CONSIDER YOURSELF SUCCESSFUL AS SOON AS YOU <u>CREATE</u> YOUR GOALS!

QUESTION:
<u>Will you require outside help, guidance, or mentoring to help facilitate this change?</u> Who can you call upon?
- ❏ A therapist?
- ❏ Health advisor? Coach? (Life coach? Personal trainer?)
- ❏ Partner? (friend at work to walk with, neighbor to share chores with, friend to take a class with you)
- ❏ Physician?
- ❏ Expert in field? (i.e. financial planner)
- ❏ Support group? (formal - i.e. Weight Watchers, AA. Or informal - a group of friends)

How will you find outside help? Ask a friend? In the phone book? Local wellness center? Online? Your physician?

PLANNING:

<u>Write your goals down. A contract is even stronger.</u>

<u>Who will be your cheerleaders? Support people?</u>

You need support people. Programs like Weight Watchers and AA are successful because members support each other. Don't make the mistake of being the "lone ranger" in your plan. Sticking to carrots and tofu while your husband happily munches on Oreos and ice cream does not constitute support. Hang out with others who share your goals.

WHO WILL BE YOUR CHEERLEADERS??
1._____
2._____
3._____
4._____
5._____

The secret of getting ahead is getting started!
~ *Sally Berger*

- Using the Wellness Wheel, examine your current state and set a goal.

- Using a journal or just a loose leaf binder, create a daily to-do list.

- Create specific goals with dates and outcomes. As in ...

Goal:
By July 1, 2007, I will have 200 volunteer hours logged in at the Women's Shelter.

Steps:
By January 15, I will call the shelter to make an appointment to discuss volunteering.
By March 1, I will begin my volunteer training.
By April 15, I will sign up for regular hours.

Small steps increase your confidence. We all love crossing things off the list, right?

Here's a more ambitious example:
You want to return to college to get a degree. You haven't been a student since high school graduation 20 years ago. Just a tad overwhelming. So here's how you eat this particular elephant, one bite at a time.

1. Start to investigate the colleges and universities nearby. And don't overlook degree courses offered online. You might be able to earn your degree in your at-home classroom!
2. Obtain the college catalogs (or the online curricula) and see what's offered and when.
3. Most community colleges offer a career planning course that includes personality and aptitude assessments. This class can be enormously helpful if you just don't know what you want to be when you grow up.
4. Will your employer or company pay for any or all of your education? You may be surprised to find out that they do.
5. Talk to a school counselor. Don't be shy ... you are the reason they have a job!
6. Begin the application process.

- Write realistic dates for each step next to each one.

Returning to school with students half my age to earn my Master's Degree was a daunting idea. Two years of this? So I started with just one or two classes to test the water. And I found that I loved it! Time really does fly when you're having fun, and pretty soon I was figuratively tossing my graduate's cap in the air and wondering how it was that the time could whiz by so fast.

STRATEGIES FOR STAYING THE COURSE
*Utilize self talk and visualization.

Imagine yourself completing your goals. Place a photograph of your head on the body-shape you desire and post it on your refrigerator door. Or place your face on a picture of a college graduate throwing his/her cap in the air. When he prepared his 10-year goals for my class, one student brought a cake decorated with congratulations on his new military rank (he would get the real one in about 7 years). My sister, who competes in cross country events, visualizes the entire race in her head before she starts. She sees herself and her horse gliding easily over each fence, and when she reaches the finish line, she hears the crowd cheering. She imagines the gold coins and rose petals at her feet (okay, I added that last part). Tell yourself you can do it; imagine the feelings of exhilaration upon completion, upon success.

STRATEGIES FOR JUMPING OVER HURDLES
Strategy 1:
Make a commitment to yourself by creating and signing a contract. Again, your goals should have specific dates, specific numbers, and be positive.

Strategy 2:
Use affirmations to inspire yourself. Affirmations are positive, present, personal. "I am calm. I am beautiful."

Strategy 3:
Call a support person, your own personal cheer leader for motivation and a hug.

Strategy 4:
Chart your progress.

Strategy 5:
Reward yourself.

Here's the best part of this chapter: you ready? You have already completed the most difficult part.

Goal:_____

_____

_____

Completion date:_____

Step 1:_____

_____

_____

Start date:_____

Completion date:_____

Step 2:_____

_____

_____

Start date:_____

Completion date:_____

Step 3:_____

_____

_____

Start date:_____

Completion date:_____

Reward:_____

Support Person:_____

Affirmation:_____

Chapter 5

Values

*Those are my principles, and if you don't like them ... well,
I have others.*
~ Groucho Marx

An episode of *Seinfeld* called "The Couch" finds Elaine and Jerry leaving Poppy's restaurant after waiting forever for a table, because Elaine discovers that Poppy supports the anti-choice movement. Jerry wants her to eat now and live by her values later. So when she begins dating a new man, Jerry challenges her: "What is his stand on abortion?" To which Elaine replies: "Well, I'm sure he's pro-choice." Jerry: "How do you know?" Elaine: "Because he, well...he's just so good-looking." Of course, it turns out he is not pro-choice. Does Elaine drop him because she stands by her values, like she did that time at Poppy's restaurant? Or does she stay with the new man because he is so good looking?

Can you overlook or accept someone or something whose values conflict with yours when the opportunity is attractive enough? Where is your own personal line in the sand? Do you know? Have you thought about your values? Is it time to start?

Values are the underlying principles, consciously and unconsciously adopted, that guide our very lives. Our values drive our choices, determine the direction, and define the friends, the fabric, and the quality of our lives. Yet, despite their monumental importance, many of us have spent little time defining, cultivating, and living by our values. Years ago, when I was teaching "diversion" classes for folks who'd been arrested and court ordered to attend, I discovered just how large the gap can be between what we value and how we actually live. It fascinated me, and I began to include values clarification in everything I teach.

In this case, I started by giving them a list of 50 core values, from which they were to choose the top 10 – the ones that shape their lives. The most common 4 among the top ten choices were: Freedom (which they lost as a result of their choices); Health (which was compromised as a result of their choices. Most of the theft clients were under the influence when arrested, or were committing crimes to support their drug habits); Honesty (yet they would lie, cheat, and steal); and Family (which they often destroyed as a result of their behavior and subsequent arrest). Can you blame me for being fascinated by this stuff? These people had to be tearing themselves apart from the inside out with the stress of living in such opposition to the things they prized the most!

One student disclosed to us the reason for his arrest. He had cleaned out his windshield wiper fluid and replaced the fluid with vodka. He then ran a clear tube from the container to the dash of the car, so he could suck on it while driving and not get arrested. Pure genius, he said. When I reminded him that Health was among his top five values, he quickly added that he also drank a gallon of orange juice to go with the vodka, "for the Vitamin C." Oh, I said. Silly me.

When I began teaching at the college level, I wanted the students to leave my classes with more than just the straight course content required by the administration. I wanted them to know that they are special and unique, that they are creative, they can pursue their dreams and live according to their core values. I set out to achieve this with some unique assignments.

One is similar to the Top Ten Values assignment I'd given to my diversion students. I ask them to list their top values and then state why they are important. At first, the students are ecstatic. "No research?" they say. "Cool." But when they turn in their papers, you should hear them whine! It isn't easy discovering that the gap between what you value and how you live is as wide as the Grand Canyon.

If I asked you to name your top core values, you would probably take a bit of time to answer. If I asked you whether you're living according to these treasured beliefs, how would you answer? You value health yet smoke 3 packs of cigarettes a day? You value family yet work 80 hours a week? You value honesty yet you occasionally fudge on your expense report? How wide is the gap between your values and your lifestyle?

Copyright 2002 by Randy Glasbergen.
www.glasbergen.com

CHILD PSYCHOLOGY

GLASBERGEN

"You're spending the best years of your life doing a job that you hate so you can buy stuff you don't need to support a lifestyle you don't enjoy. Sounds crazy to me!"

Another assignment I give is something called the "dream collage." I bring stacks of magazines and ask them to thumb through and pull out the pictures that speak to them. Don't think too much about each choice, I instruct them. Just keep whatever catches your attention. Next they create a collage of their pictures and words. And finally, they write a paper explaining what the collages mean to them. Most collages I get are on foam core board, but I had one submitted on the top of a drum, another submitted inside a large cut-out of the word "peace", and one on a pizza box. (He owned a pizza parlor.) Many students use stickers, glitter, photographs, all sorts of fun little treasures. Some of these have been downright exquisite.

Dream print by Jennifer Olsen

Next, I ask the students to answer the following questions: What does your collage say about you? Your values? Your dreams and hopes for the future? Explain your choices, what the pictures you chose mean to you. Why do you have so many pictures of animals...children... trees... the ocean? What in the collage represents what makes you happy? Why, if this was hanging on the wall in the class, would it represent YOU rather than anyone else? If your friends and family came in and looked at the 50 collages on the wall, would they be able to pick yours out? How?

Ask yourself

What are your core values? Are you living your life according to these values? Did you choose these values freely or did others choose for you? Do you feel comfortable standing up for these values? Consistently?

I believe you need to examine your values before you can really start on a program of moving toward wellness. What are your beliefs about how to live your life? What is most important to you?

Try creating a dream print, examine your values, and then ask yourself: Am I living my life accordingly? What do I need to change to do so?

Chapter 6

Gratitude

To educate yourself for the feeling of gratitude means to take nothing for granted, but to always seek out and value the kind that will stand behind the action. Nothing that is done for you is a matter of course. Everything originates in a will for the good, which is directed at you. Train yourself never to put off the word or action for the expression of gratitude.
~ *Albert Schweitzer*

My friend Arlene at Methodist Hospital in Arcadia told me a wonderful story about a client of hers. One afternoon she walked into her office and a woman was there, in her 60's, in a wheelchair. It turned out the woman, Bonnie, had been paralyzed from the neck down 50 years earlier as the result of having polio. She shared a bit about her life, that she was busy taking care of her many elderly friends. Arlene was curious. She hadn't seen the woman enter her office, and she knew she was completely paralyzed, yet she didn't have the usual device (quadraplegics can be taught to blow air into a mechanism that will move the chair). So how did she get around? "I'm am so lucky," she replied. "When I had polio, everything stopped working except my left foot. I use it to move my chair." She's completely paralyzed, she's on a ventilator 24 hours a day, and she feels lucky her foot is fine? Now *that's* what I call gratitude. Arlene says, whenever she is having a bad day she wiggles her left foot and smiles.

Wikipedia tells us that – "Gratitude, appreciation, or thankfulness, is an emotion, which involves a feeling of emotional indebtedness towards another person; often accompanied by a desire to thank them, or to reciprocate for a favor they have done for you." Research has also suggested that feelings of gratitude may be beneficial to subjective emotional well-being (Emmons & McCullough, 2003). "In people who are grateful in general, life events have little influence on experienced gratitude."

I respectfully suggest that gratitude extends beyond other people. Feelings of gratitude can be felt and expressed for all kinds of non-human things and conditions: Health, beauty, music, art, nature, even the weather. Say thank you to whomever you like for these things, but say it.

I fully acknowledge that my upbringing makes it easier for me to be appreciative. Growing up in Ethiopia gave me an appreciation in technicolor for all that we (Americans) have on so many levels. This does not mean that just because you grew up sheltered from those who have less, you are off the hook. On the contrary. You just need more practice.

It is easy to spend much of our day complaining, forgetting to be appreciative. Well, Pastor Will Bowen has a cure for that. *People Magazine* ran a terrific article about this man and his purple plastic bracelets. Inscribed with the words "A Complaint Free World,"

© 2001 Randy Glasbergen.
www.glasbergen.com

"This morning I almost didn't get a doughnut, later somebody put me on hold for three minutes, and then I got a paper cut! *My life is unbearable!*"

Pastor Bowen challenged his congregation to wear them. He instructed them to switch the bracelet from left to right wrist (or vice versa) every time they complained or gossiped (or caught a fellow parishioner doing it). The goal was to keep the bracelet unmoved for 21 days – the number of days it takes to create a habit. I immediately wrote the good Pastor and ordered enough purple plastic bracelets for my wellness class at Allan Hancock College. What an amazing class assignment!

I end each day with a mental list of the things I am thankful for. I ask my students on a regular basis to state out loud just one thing they are grateful for. Saying it out loud makes it more real somehow. Asking you to practice being grateful in no way dismisses the pain, the difficulties, or the losses in our lives. But gratitude helps to soothe the pain, diffuses the difficulties, and gives meaning to the losses.

One of the best remedies for a case of the pity-pot blues is the movie "Life is Beautiful." I challenge you to watch that movie and continue to feel sorry for yourself. This Oscar-winning movie is an object lesson in making lemonade out of lemons.

Things that make me laugh...

Friends

_____

_____

_____

_____

_____

_____

Movies/TV

_____

_____

_____

_____

_____

_____

Cartoons

_____

_____

_____

_____

_____

_____

Activities

_____

_____

_____

_____

_____

_____

My Gratitude List...

*If the only prayer you said in your whole life was, "thank you,"
that would suffice.*
~ Meister Eckhart

_____

_____

_____

_____

_____

_____

_____

_____

_____

_____

_____

_____

_____

_____

_____

_____

_____

_____

_____

_____

_____

_____

_____

_____

*Appreciation can make a day, even change a life. Your willingness
to put it into words is all that is necessary.*
~ Margaret Cousins

Chapter 7

Passion-Filled Work

Loathing Monday is a sad way to spend one-seventh of your life.
~ Unknown

The secret of success is making your vocation your vacation.
~ Mark Twain

I never did a day's work in my life; it was all fun.
~ Thomas Edison

Only 1 in 3 Americans love what they do for a living. Are you one of them? Well, here's a heads up. If you are among the other two-thirds whose work is just a job, I have no sympathy. Because whether you believe me or not, the work you do is your choice. What have you chosen? Does your career excite you? Are you happy and satisfied with the work you do? Is it challenging and fulfilling? Does it bring you joy? Are you living a life you love? No? Then read on, McDuff. Help is on the way.

(And if you are happy in the work you have chosen, does that mean you can skip this chapter? Absolutely not. Why? Because what makes you happy today may not make you happy tomorrow. The only certainty in life is change. Weeks, months, or years from now you may need to know how to make a critical career change.)

The average workweek has grown here in America from 40 hours to 50, 60, sometimes even 70 or 80 hours a week. It's not uncommon to hear people say (with some degree of pride, though I wonder why?!) that they spent many years working 70-hour workweeks. Add to that the number of hours we sit over drinks with colleagues discussing work, the time it takes to commute to work, and the times we lie awake at 3 a.m. thinking about work – we had better be loving it!

"We also have some part-time positions available for people who only want to work 60 or 80 hours a week."

I do love my job. Even if I won millions in the lottery, why would I want to stop doing what I love? Work feels more like play than work and I do realize how lucky I am. Is it really just luck, though, or is there something else going on? Looking back, I will admit that my earliest jobs were not that high on the fun chart. In college, I worked eight hours a day stuffing envelopes. Not my dream job by any stretch, but we had fun. We laughed, we sang, we enjoyed each other. And *that* was a choice. You can choose to enjoy any job, and if they don't allow it, you can leave it. Yes, you can!

Anne Lamott, one of my favorite authors, wrote a book called "Plan B." I am big on backup plans. Having a backup plan (preferably more than one) for jobs does wonders for one's attitude. Plan B offers you freedom, choice, and serenity – even when you find yourself in the Land of the Cursed (OK Anne used a different word from *cursed!*) some days. Plan B gives you the freedom to simply quit if your boss is an inflexible jerk, or the nature of the work becomes too stressful, mean-spirited, or boring. There is no need to compromise your happiness, your sanity, or your integrity by staying in a job that makes you miserable.

I once quit a job I didn't like much. My boss just didn't believe me when I warned him that if I wasn't happy, I'd quit. He smirked in that really annoying, self-righteous way and said that if being happy was a requirement, most people would not have jobs. Two weeks after I quit, he emailed me that he thought I was kidding, right? I wasn't. By the way, my Plan B is waitressing. Knowing I can pick up a serving position just about anywhere, any time, gives me the freedom to wave goodbye to bosses like him.

Here is one of the best lessons in job satisfaction I have come across. I was teaching classes for a full week at a California hospital, and was hearing a lot of frustration and complaining from the staff. That same week, I got a request to spend a few hours with an organiza-

tion that ran group homes for develop- mentally disabled adults. They had three homes, with eight clients in each. In order to have all staff attend my presentation, we all assembled at one of the homes. The staff had to transport 16 of their clients and situate them in an adjoin- ing room. The logis- tics were daunting. Before I began,

they held a short staff meeting. One item was the announcement that staff members could study and obtain certification on their own time for this specialized field. If they chose to do so, they'd get a raise to $8 an hour. Did I hear that right? Was it $8 more an hour? No. Their pay would be raised to $8 an hour, which means they were making less than that to care for this needy population of adult clients! The rest of the meeting was spent teaching them how to deal with clients who bit them and pulled their hair. Ever had that training? Ever needed it? Well they did. These events were a common hazard that came with the job...*and* they were not making $8 an hour...*and* they were wonderful, happy people. Back at the hospital job the following day, I shared this story and let them know that today would not be a good day for me to hear their grumbling. My sympathy level had dropped considerably.

At another hospital, I met a new nurse, fresh out of school, in my leadership class for nurse managers. At her request, I had given her special permission to attend. During the class she declared how much she loved her job, that she was delighted to be making a difference, and looked forward to coming to work every day. One of the more seasoned nurses commented, "You can sure tell she is new." And everyone laughed — except the new nurse. About 5 minutes later she raised her hand again and said, "I know some of you think I am young and hopelessly naïve. But I want you to know that my attitude is my choice. If you find me in 10, even 20 years, I promise you I will still love what I do; and I will always be aware that I'm making a difference." I believe her. I believe that this young nurse will always be a shining example of positivism — because she knows it's her choice.

Ask Yourself:

Do you have a passion for the work you do? Do the hours fly by? This optimal experience is called flow, where joy, creativity and total involvement with life happens and you are in the "zone" - a term coined by Mihaly Csikszentmihalyi. (I didn't really have to add his name, but admit it: You are just a little impressed that I know his name. And yes, I can pronouce it.) In the "zone" it's hard for people to get your attention; you forget to take a lunch break; and you look at the clock and realize five hours have passed. The best part? You produce phenomenal results!

There is a continuum (known as Neulinger's Paradigm, another impressive add in) where pure leisure exists at one end, and pure job at the other. The primary difference lies in the motivation. Your task is to determine whether your motivation is intrinsic or extrinsic. Do you work from an internal source of motivation, for its own sake? Or do you work for external rewards like approval or a paycheck?

If you won the lottery tomorrow and quit your job, what would you miss the most? The Wright Brothers were quoted as saying they couldn't wait to get up in the morning. Do you have to invent something as monumental as the airplane to be excited about your work?

Don't believe you can re-invent your life? Well listen up. Here are the stories of two gals I met at different trainings. Darcie is a vet at an animal shelter where I've done some training. She's a lively, animated, caring woman whom you like immediately. I asked how long she had been a vet and she told me that when she turned 40 she was working as an eligibility worker with social services. But she'd dreamed her whole life of becoming a vet. It was now or never. She was accepted at UC Davis, one of the best and most difficult programs to get into.

I met the fabulous Melanie at a speaking gig for the "National Women in Construction" conference. At lunch, Melanie told me she's a contractor. And I just had to ask her how in the world an Asian female had ended up in the construction industry. Had it been a family business? Nope. She had spent years as a pediatric oncologist! And after all those years of education, she found it to be a heartbreaking career and decided to ... become a builder instead.

If you love your job passionately, "Right on!" If you don't, use Darcie or Melanie as role models and do something about it. It is never too late, and there are no good excuses.

Chapter 8

Assumptions

We simply assume that the way we see things is the way they really are or the way they should be. And our attitudes and behaviors grow out of these assumptions.
~ Stephen R. Covey

Assumptions allow the best in life to pass you by.
~ John Sales

Assume, and you make an ass out of you and me.
~ Unknown

I once had a friend share with me that her son shaves his head and has a number of tattoos and piercings. One Sunday morning at church, a woman standing beside her whispered, "Will you look at that awful gang banger. What is he doing here?" I would have given a week's salary to trade places with the fly on the wall when my friend replied, "Oh, you mean my son, who makes me come to church even when I am too tired because he wants to praise our Lord?"

We make assumptions about everything. It's part of the human condition; we can't live without them. The trick is to determine which assumptions are useful and which ones are harmful. Assumptions about other people, based on looks, color, or body art can be harmful to everyone, including the assumer. My guess is that the woman who assumed my friend's son was a gang banger learned more than what was taught in the sermon that day.

One of the major discussions we have in my *Using Good Judgment* course is all about assumptions. Simply defined, an assumption is a belief that something is true without proof or demonstration. We make assumptions based on data culled from our life experiences. We couldn't live our lives without making them. Assumptions help us gather information to make sense of the world around us. For example, I assume that other drivers run red lights, so I never head out across the intersection the second my light turns green. In that case, assuming could save my life.

Here are some common assumptions: that people will cooperate; that you understand others' motives or agendas and they understand yours; that people listen; that you will be recognized for outstanding work; that things won't get done unless you do it. Sound familiar? How about the assumptions people make on the job, like: Cops assume people will lie; electricians assume all wires are hot, etc. Those assumptions can save lives.

We also sometimes assume that people have the same values as we do. Here's a good example: One day I shared a story with my students about a friend who'd had a horrific experience with her vet. A mistake was made that resulted in having to put her beloved dog to sleep. "What's the big deal?" asked one of the boys in my class. "She can always get another dog." I had assumed (key word) that everyone would have empathy and I was shocked by his comment.

And here's a good one: When I began teaching at the college level, I assumed that all students were there to learn, to become educated, to get an "A." Not so.

Other assumptions are situational. When you assume someone is mad at you because they walked by your office this morning and didn't say hello, ask yourself if this is a reasonable assumption and even better, *ask them*. The way to handle assumptions is to communicate. Ask questions. It probably isn't even about you. Big shock, I know.

Along with these assumptions about life, we also make assumptions about ourselves. As children, we assume things about ourselves but forget to conduct a reality check when we grow up. When we carry around self-assumptions that aren't true anymore, we can seriously impede our ability to reach our full potential. I'm amazed at how long some antiquated ideas about gender can persist. In a class I teach about *Finding Your Passion* people often tell me that they "can't" pursue a certain career because "it's a woman's field" or "a man's job." How about "women aren't good at math" and "men are not empathetic." These assumptions are outdated and hold us back.

Some of us also assume we have certain limitations – usually judgments we hear from others that we then internalize. We assume we are "shy" or "clumsy" or "skinny" or "stupid." We assume we don't have support (before we even ask); we assume we've done everything possible (when there are other options available). We even assume "it's happened before, so it will happen again," begging trouble in our relationships.

Use the worksheet to list the assumptions you make about yourself. Then ask yourself: Is it true? Why do you believe this to be true about yourself? Where did you get this message? What are the potential results of this assumption? Does it stop you from reaching your full potential?

I'm willing to bet that many of these assumptions are not, in fact, the truth about you. Won't it be great to discard them? Optimal wellness is just around the corner ... and letting go of old, useless assumptions will get you there a lot quicker.

Assumptions I make about myself:

Assumption #1: Where did I get this idea? Is it true? Is this assumption helpful?   Is it hurting me?

_____

_____

_____

Assumption #2: Where did I get this idea? Is it true? Is this assumption helpful?   Is it hurting me?

_____

_____

_____

Assumption #3: Where did I get this idea? Is it true? Is this assumption helpful?   Is it hurting me?

_____

_____

_____

_____

Assumption #4: Where did I get this idea? Is it true? Is this assumption helpful?   Is it hurting me?

_____

_____

_____

Assumption #5: Where did I get this idea? Is it true? Is this assumption helpful?   Is it hurting me?

_____

_____

_____

Chapter 9

Leisure & Play

If you can't learn to do it well,
learn to enjoy doing it badly.
~ Ashleigh Brilliant

You are never too old to do goofy stuff.
~ Ward Clever from "Leave it to Beaver"

You can never have too many feather boas.
~ Jean Steel

Stop! Please don't skip this chapter. If you are even thinking of skipping this chapter, then you are the one who needs it most. Why? Because you don't think play is important. Because you already make very good use of your leisure time, thank you very much.

Perhaps you do. But do you remember what it feels like to be a peg-legged pirate or a flying fairy queen? Do you give yourself the time to get "lost" in time? When was the last time you got very dirty, and didn't care? Or yelled "Ollie Ollie Oxen Free" at the top of your lungs? Danced around the house in your underwear ... or made a toy cabin out of popsicle sticks?

Color-coding your sock drawer and entering data into your Quicken program does not qualify as "leisure." Leisure is not a luxury in a balanced life; it's a necessity. So listen up!

45

Playing ...

- gives you the opportunity to examine your personal values, to focus on what is important to you.
- gives you the balance you need to deal with your non-leisure activities, like work and bills and cleaning and errands ...
- gives you needed relief from stress and boredom, helping promote better physical and mental health. Can you say *wellness?*
- buffers the effects of stress and reduces stress-related illnesses.

Not playing ...

- makes you a sorry, boring, illness-prone, stressed out stick-in-the-mud. So there!

I have a master's degree in playing, honest! I knew I wanted to teach a brand new way of looking at wellness and I was given permission to design my own program. When it came time to choose which department would oversee my studies, I chose *Recreation and Leisure* – for two reasons. One, because you simply cannot call your life balanced if all you do is work. All work and no play ... well, you know the rest. And two, because the department head, Steve Gray, did not call himself Dr. anything. His name was listed after the title "Supreme Commander." Now that's who I wanted to work with! My instincts were right on. This guy embodies the concept of wellness. He's a great teacher, a fabulous mentor, and he's very funny. But not as funny as me.

Whenever I ask a class full of adults how often they play, I get really weak answers. Ask a classroom full of kids and they can't wait to tell me! What happens between ages 4 and 24 that causes us to lose our ability to play? What is our problem? Is it guilt? Lack of time? Lack of energy? Are we too stressed? Too competitive? Too poor? Do we have the wrong attitude? A stifling work ethic? Are we not willing to look silly? Or have we just forgotten how?

Well here is a crash course. It's called *The Art of Playing 101*, and there are three assignments. And yes, there will homework later. (You didn't really think this chapter was going to be all fun and games, did you?)

1.) The Observation Task: Observe children under eight years old at play for at least a half hour. Visit a playground or schoolyard and get permission from the adult in charge. Write down your observations. Following this task, one of my students wrote this:

"Although the children on the average playground are not in some ways as learned as their adult counterparts, children on the whole seem to possess a knowledge about selfhood that should make them the envy of the adult community; lauded as practitioners of true wisdom." See for yourself!

2.) The Discovery Task: Choose an activity you've never done before; something out of your comfort zone. No, not skydiving necessarily, but how about kite flying, or gourmet cooking? Do it once, and then write about it, answering the questions at the end of this chapter. Expanding our repertoire of favorite activities keeps the art of playing fresh and more fun. Here are a few other suggestions inspired by my students: Play bingo at your grandmother's retirement home, attend a psychic fair, take a bonsai class, go star-gazing with an astronomer. So many things...so little time.

3.) The Play Day Assignment: Give yourself a play day. Yup. A whole day away from the grind, dedicated to the sole purpose of having fun. It would be ideal if you can engage others in this play day. Have a picnic, play croquet or charades or miniature golf. Spend the day on the beach chasing the waves and playing silly word games. Whatever you like. The laughter, the bonding, the teamwork, the acting silly ... you're gonna love it! Who knows? Maybe you'll start a tradition.

Don't think you can pull it off? Take heart. I've been hired by many organizations to conduct play retreats for their staff. One was a biotech firm and I was reluctant to take the job. Do Ph.D. chemists want to play? Their HR manager assured me they did, then later admitted they'd rather eat glass. I had my work (er, my play) cut out for me! Well, you just haven't lived 'till you've watched a bunch of buttoned-down scientists shoving marshmallows in their mouths while shouting "chubby bunny." Listen, if a Ph.D. chemist can play, so can you.

Television is by far and away the biggest culprit in the decline of play in America. I grew up without one, so I continue to enjoy the dying practice of reading ... books. Sure, I enjoy TV, but it can be a dangerous way to spend your time. Orson Wells once said: "I hate television. I hate it as much as peanuts. But I can't stop eating peanuts."

So put down that remote and go play. Check out your city's recreation departments, community college adult education classes, the public library, the local little theater.

Johns Hopkins found that people who engage in a variety of pastimes seem to have a better chance of warding off dementia. They also discovered that elderly people who engage in social activities live longer than more reclusive people. A fourth task for this chapter is to fill out the page titled *20 Fun Things You Love to Do*. Next to each one, write down whether you can do it alone or with others? Is it free or does it cost money? Does is require planning, or can it be done spontaneously? And finally, when did you last do this activity?

If you love camping and the last time you went was six years ago ... if you love baking and your last cake came out of the oven in 1992 ... if kayaking brings you bliss but you haven't been on the water since your second kid was born ... well, I double dare you to change all that.

As George Bernard Shaw wisely said, "We don't stop playing because we grow old; we grow old because we stop playing."

My goal for you in this chapter is to give yourself permission to relax, to play, to do goofy stuff.

WORKSHEETS

ASK YOURSELF...
- o What factors influence my leisure behavior (or lack there of)?
- o What are some of my barriers to leisure?
- o Do I let my stressors get in the way of my leisure enjoyment?
- o Does having time on my hands make me feel uncomfortable?
- o Do I ever feel guilty for enjoying myself and relaxing?
- o Are there are lots of leisure activities I'd like to do but I doubt I will ever do them?
- o Have I given the same amount of thought to leisure as I do to my work/career?
- o Do my leisure activities provide me with an avenue for self-expression that my work does not?
- o How playful am I? And how much of that is from how I was raised?
- o Do I use where I live as an excuse for not doing the things I love more often?
- o Do I try to broaden my leisure interests as I grow older?
- o Do I enjoy planning and anticipating the event as much as the activity itself?
- o Are the leisure activities I enjoy most typical for those of my gender (male or female)?
- o Do I worry what others will say if I am silly or playful?

20 SUPER FUN THINGS I LOVE TO DO

List the activity & last date you did the activity.

1. _____
2. _____
3. _____
4. _____
5. _____
6. _____
7. _____
8. _____
9. _____
10. _____
11. _____
12. _____
13. _____
14. _____
15. _____
16. _____
17. _____
18. _____
19. _____
20. _____

CIRCLE THE ONES YOU'D LIKE TO TRY:

Book Club	Camping	Gardening
Walking	Yoga	Listening to Music
Dinner Party	Team Sports	Watch Sporting Events
Sewing	Quilting	Golf
Crafts	Cake Decorating	Dancing
Cooking	Playing Cards	Hiking
Bicycling	Going to a play/theater	Sporting Events
Motorcycling	Skiing	Woodworking
Skating	Kayaking	Working on cars
Writing	Boating	Animals
Bowling	Painting	Running
Horseback riding	Tennis	Traveling
Acting	Windsurfing	Hang Gliding
Archery	Scuba Diving	Spa Weekend
Photography	Rowing	Treasure Hunting
Swimming	Picnicking	Collecting
Bird watching	Museum	Furniture Refinishing
Adult Education	Snorkeling	Musical Instrument
Aerobics	Ceramics	Genealogy
Karaoke	Volleyball	Pilates
Martial Arts	Songwriting	Tennis

THE DISCOVERY TASK QUESTIONS:

1. What was the event, when did it occur, and where?
2. Why did you choose this particular activity?
3. What were your expectations prior to the activity?
4. What emotional responses did you experience as the event approached?
5. Describe the actual event.
6. What emotional responses did you experience during the event?
7. What emotional responses did you experience following the event?
8. How could the event have been better?
9. To what extent will this event be part of your leisure in the future?
10. What potential for your personal growth and development did this activity hold for you?
11. What did you learn about yourself?

Okay. Class dismissed. It's recess ... now what are you going to do?

Chapter 10

Humor & Laughter

The most wasted of all days is one without laughter.
~ e.e. cummings

Laughter is an instant vacation.
~ Milton Berle

What soap is to the body, laughter is to the soul.
~ Yiddish proverb

Kindergartners laugh about 300 times a day. Adults 17. I know I have the kindergartners beat. How about you?

When was the last time you laughed? No. I mean tears running down your face, can't breathe, doubled over, stomach hurts kind of laughed?

Laughter makes you feel better...no kidding. Scientific studies have shown that laughter...

- lowers the level of Cortisol, one of those nasty stress hormones
- helps us to cope. Seeing humor in a situation is one of the most important coping devices we have. If you can laugh at it, you can handle it.
- lightens your load by providing perspective. If we can laugh about it, it can't be that bad. As Chaplin said, "Life is a tragedy when seen in close-up, but a comedy in the long shot."
- stimulates the immune system.
- lowers blood pressure.
- reduces pain.
- brings people together.
- improves creativity.

**"You probably came in contact with
someone who has an infectious smile."**

Negativity cannot survive humor. It is impossible to be angry or stressed while laughing. For me, it's a survival mechanism. My sister uses laughter as her own personal crisis barometer: if she can't laugh about it, she knows she is on overload.

Why don't we laugh more? One issue is that we all have such different senses of humor, different ideas about what's funny and what's not. When I went to see "Raising Arizona" I could not contain myself. I just howled with laughter, the solo voice in a half-filled theater. These people don't find this stuff funny? I couldn't understand it. And I'm sure they all thought I was crazy, too.

I received the news of my father's Alzheimer's diagnosis, along with my mother and three sisters and brother, at the Alzheimer's Center at UC Davis. Naturally, we were devastated. The social worker told us she knew we'd be okay. She'd been watching us during Dad's three-day evaluation ordeal and had witnessed our ability to laugh easily and often. Our collective sense of humor kept us sane.

I am not suggesting that we learn to laugh off all our problems. There was nothing funny about this diagnosis. But there were some very funny moments, and we found we had a choice. We could laugh or we could cry; we chose the former.

Research suggests that a humorous outlook increases our ability to more effectively manage emotional distress—thereby reducing the damaging physical impact of stress.

Tips
- Smile. Even if you don't feel like it, smile anyway. Studies prove that soon enough you will feel happier.
- Watch yourself and what you laugh at, and then find ways to support that sense of humor. I laugh at kids – their antics, their stories, their silliness.
- Find authors, books, and cartoonists that make you laugh. The humor in one of my favorite books, *Stupid and Contagious* by the fabulous Caprice Crane, is laugh-out-loud funny. For different funny bones, there's the sardonic but equally funny Anne Lamott's *Operating Instructions*. A passage in the latter caught me stifling one of those explosive laugh-snorts one time on an airplane. (My poor seat mate.)
- I give humor breaks on my college final exams. Questions 1 through 5 are followed by a couple of one-liners from great comedy writers like Dave Barry. Complete questions 6 through 10, and there's another little laugh break. And so on.
- Bring laughter into the workplace: Post cartoons, share funny stories at staff meetings, get tickets to a comedy show. When I worked as the Wellness Coordinator at MCI WorldCom, I got a fantastic deal to buy out the local Comedy Club and sold the tickets to staff (over 200) in half an hour. Everyone wanted to go.
- Include laughs in your email messages. Not canned jokes, but something that will make people at the other end smile. I once had a problem with a vendor, so I sent them an e-mail

expressing my frustration, but I did it in a humorous way. They wrote back, proclaiming my e-mail the funniest of the week and guess what? I got what I needed from them.

- Have friends over to watch a favorite comedy (*Harold and Maude, Christopher Guest,* and old *Seinfeld* episodes are tried-and-true laugh machines for me) or play a fun game – like Charades. No, I mean it. That old game needs absolutely nothing but your imagination, and it's guaranteed to make you laugh. Even unfunny people get laughs.

- Hang out with happy, funny people. You know the ones!

And listen, next time someone gives you an eye roll or tells you to put a sock in it, just remember what Martin Luther used to say: "If I am not allowed to laugh in heaven, I don't want to go there."

WORKSHEET

List of favorite funny films:

_____   _____
_____   _____
_____   _____
_____   _____
_____   _____
_____   _____
_____   _____
_____   _____
_____   _____
_____   _____
_____   _____
_____   _____

List of people you can call who always make you laugh:

_____   _____
_____   _____
_____   _____
_____   _____
_____   _____
_____   _____
_____   _____
_____   _____
_____   _____
_____   _____
_____   _____
_____   _____

Chapter 11

Creativity

There are painters who transform the sun to a yellow spot, but there are others who, with the help of their art and their intelligence, transform a yellow spot into the sun.
~ Pablo Picasso

Happiness is not in the mere possession of money; it lies in the joy of achievement, in the thrill of creative effort.
~ Franklin Roosevelt

A professor I use to work with told me of an interesting study he replicated. A black dot was put on a white board, and a group of kindergartners was asked what it was. Very few said a black dot. They said that dot was everything from a squashed bug, to a booger, to a hole through the board. When college students were asked the same thing most said it was...a black dot. I replicated it again with my college class and from a field of over 100 students, only about 5 said it was something other than a black dot. One said it was a hole into an alternative universe and yes, one of them saw a booger. As for the other 95? Since when did older and wiser have to mean boring and unimaginative? Can't we be older, wiser, adventurous and creative, too?

Creativity is the ability to make connections, to see new relationships and links. Creativity is our birthright; we're born with it. Now I know that the evidence of your creative life thus far may foster some serious doubts about this fact. To whit, that snazzy haircut you gave your three-year-old sister; "when you were five" the clover-leaf ashtray you made for Father's Day in the third grade. How about the volcano you built for the 8th grade science fair, or the happenin' outfit you assembled for Senior Picture Day? Even the cake you decorated for your daughter's 5th birthday was a disaster! I won't argue with you. We are not creative in every modality and medium. But all of us have something we're creatively good at. The trick is to discover and nurture it. For example, when my Uncle John retired from his career as a prominent surgeon, my Aunt Jean signed him up for painting classes. She was tired of having him constantly underfoot. Never a painter, Uncle John discovered he had a gift for it, a talent good enough to sell. Soon, this 60-year-old man who never knew he had any artistic talent, had a studio full of finished paintings and a lucrative second career.

My sister Suzie, the artist for the wonderful pictures in this book, used to throw away her drawings because they weren't perfect – paintings you and I would hang on our walls with pride. To be creative, you must free yourself of rules, restrictions and restraints. Self-judgment and criticism kills our creativity and murders our best work. Teachers and professors are the worst offenders. One of my college students reluctantly agreed to show me his paintings one day. The work was so stunning it took my breath away, yet hardly anyone even knew he painted. He confided that one of his art professors had laughed at his work and he'd walked home crying, devastated. If she'd still been on campus, I would have given her a piece of my mind. I will never understand why teachers deliberately choose to be unkind.

When he started kindergarten, my nephew Tony was a dapper dresser. His first day he wore a double-breasted suit jacket, shirt and tie...and soccer shorts. Soon after, he began to create a different hairstyle every day, and name it. To the amusement of his teacher he created "stormy waters, road with spikes, electric hair, flaming highway and road through junk yard." Would this creativity fly if his dad, a chemical engineer, replicated it?

I fill my trainings and classes with creative activities. One of my favorites? I pass out three pipe cleaners to each participant and ask them to create something. They have the entire session (maximum 4 hours) to create while I am talking, with some amazing results. One recent winning entry was a pink poodle with a black collar and leash, holding his leg up over a red fire hydrant – from the West Coast Athletic Club no less! This is the same group who months earlier broke into groups, took a normal household or office item and found dozens of alternative uses for them. I never knew there could be so many uses for a staple remover. (Don't ask.)

Every semester, I am unendingly surprised by the creative presentations my students turn in for their 5-, 10-, and 15-year dreams and life goals projects. Just when I think I have seen it all, they blow me out of the water with their creative talent, all the while whining how they are so not creative.

Benefits of Creativity

- It makes life more fun.
- Seeing new relationships and links, you become better at solving life's problems.
- You develop greater self-confidence.
- You boost your sense of humor as you learn to see incongruities in situations.
- It generates the ability to see a large number of possible solutions and ideas.
- It helps you maintain an open mind and a sense of curiosity.

Eliminate the barriers to creativity. Why you can't be creative ... any sound familiar?

- You are a practical adult.
- You are just not creative.
- You don't want to look silly.
- You're afraid of failing.

How to jump-start your creativity

- Be free – give yourself permission to be creative.
  I have students write what they want in life for 5 minutes.
  The only rules are: they may not lift their pencil from the
  paper, they may not read their work, they must keep writing.
  Why? Because if we stop, we tend to critique and edit
  ourselves, to cross things out, to judge what we have done.
  Let it flow; you will surprise yourself.
- Get some clay, work with colorful pipe cleaners, squeeze
  icing onto a cake and just play! One of my students colors
  when she is stressed. It's a great way to start your creative
  juices.
- Take art classes through your local recreation department.
- Think of a problem and come up with 10 creative solutions to
  the problem. How many would work?
- Brainstorm a solution to a problem with colleagues or friends.
  Brainstorming is the free-fall of ideas to solve problems. No
  idea is rejected, no matter how irrelevant or grandiose it
  seems until it has been thoroughly evaluated.
- Get inspired by others' creativity. The Central Coast of
  California (where I live) boasts an artist's palette of creative
  festivals – from *I Madonnari*, where they paint the sidewalk
  with vivid, gorgeous chalk paintings, to sand castle-building
  competitions, a simply jaw-hanging event! In New York City,
  architects and engineers compete to see whose team can
  build the most spectacular structure using little more than cans
  of food – at the annual "Canstruction" event.

Some believe that our educational system stifles our creativity, as witnessed in the touching, yet eye-opening lyrics to "Flowers Are Red"
from the mega-talented Harry Chapin.

Flowers are Red

by Harry Chapin

The little boy went first day of school
He got some crayons and started to draw
He put colors all over the paper
For colors was what he saw
And the teacher said, What you doin' young man
I'm paintin' flowers he said
She said... It's not the time for art young man
And anyway flowers are green and red
There's a time for everything young man
And a way it should be done
You've got to show concern for everyone else
For you're not the only one
And she said...
Flowers are red young man
Green leaves are green
There's no need to see flowers any other way
Than the way they always have been seen
But the little boy said...
There are so many colors in the rainbow
So many colors in the morning sun
So many colors in the flower and I see every one
Well the teacher said.. You're sassy
There's ways that things should be
And you'll paint flowers the way they are
So repeat after me ...
And she said...
Flowers are red young man
Green leaves are green

There's no need to see flowers any other way
Than the way they always have been seen
But the little boy said...
There are so many colors in the rainbow
So many colors in the morning sun
So many colors in the flower and I see every one
The teacher put him in a corner
She said, It's for your own good...
And you won't come out 'til you get it right
And are responding like you should
Well finally he got lonely
Frightened thoughts filled his head
And he went up to the teacher
And this is what he said.. and he said
Flowers are red, green leaves are green
There's no need to see flowers any other way
Than the way they always have been seen
Time went by like it always does
And they moved to another town
And the little boy went to another school
And this is what he found
The teacher there was smilin'
She said...Painting should be fun
And there are so many colors in a flower
So let's use every one
But that little boy painted flowers
In neat rows of green and red
And when the teacher asked him why
This is what he said.. and he said
Flowers are red, green leaves are green
There's no need to see flowers any other way
Than the way they always have been seen.

Be creative in how you live, dress, show appreciation and self-expression. There is a woman in Santa Maria, California known as the purple lady. She is over 85 now, and you can pretty easily pick her out of crowd. She has purple hair, glasses, pantsuit, socks and shoes. Yes, even a purple bra.

I once purchased some wonderful mermaid Christmas ornaments that I hated to put away after the holidays. So I got a piece of driftwood and screwed it to the wall so my mermaids could hang from it, in all their glory...all year round. They make me smile.

"I *am* dressed for success! Of course, my idea of
success may not be exactly the same as yours."

I want to thank Ernie Olson, professor extraordinaire from Sacramento State University, for allowing me to use information on creativity from his book *Personal Development and Discovery through Leisure*. Ernie would change his name each semester and allow you to change yours. Why not? He would also come teach swing dancing to my wellness students, draw wonderful cartoons and host comedy nights at the local club. Practices what he preaches, my buddy Ernie, wouldn't you say?

Check out these amazingly creative people...
- Painting on hands http://www.guidodaniele.com/
- Dirty car art (yes, you have to see it to believe it) at http://www.dirtycarart.com/
- Toilet paper wedding dress competition at http://www.cheap-chic-weddings.com/wedding-contest-2006.html
- Duck Brand duct tape has an annual contest for who can make the best prom clothes out of yes, duct tape. http://www.stuckatprom.com/contests/prom/entries.asp
- Check out the National Ice Carving Association website at http://www.nica.org/
- Finally, the amazing Optical illusion chalk drawings of Julian Beever at http://users.skynet.be/J.Beever/pave.htm

Chapter 12

Saying No

To know oneself, one should assert oneself.
~ Albert Camus

In one of the many great episodes of the TV show *Friends*, the character Joey asks his five best pals to help him move. One of them, Phoebe, responds by saying "Oh, I wish I could; but I really don't want to." The audience roars with laughter (and so do we) because Phoebe is expressing how she honestly feels, how most of us honestly feel when someone asks for help moving. And yet, we aren't supposed to be *that* honest. I ask you...why not?

In our quest for wellness, one of the most important elements is the ability to draw healthy boundaries, to learn the art of assertiveness, to say "No." The trouble is, we are so invested in making sure we are well-liked, that others approve of us, that we are thought of as nice people, that saying no has become a lost art. In fact, in some minds, saying no is equated with being selfish, uncaring, even mean. It's time to educate, cultivate, and re-instate this essential element of wellness before we all drown in a quagmire of dishonest "niceness."

Remember Nancy Reagan's "Just Say No" program, aimed at keeping kids from using drugs? I was once hired to teach that program and since I knew that most kids were too sophisticated for such a simplistic approach, I decided instead to teach the foundation for saying no: assertiveness.

In college, I discovered the best book I've yet to come across on the subject – *Your Perfect Right* by Alberti and Emmons. I knew it would capture the kids' attention because it's such an empowering concept, but I got a surprise bonus. When the topic was assertiveness,

69

their teachers – grateful to have me as their "guest teacher" so they could take a break, read the paper, have a well earned cup of coffee – paid attention. Whoa. Why would these teachers be interested in assertiveness training? Hadn't they already learned this lesson? Nope, not really. Turns out that men and women of all ages struggle with this issue. Assertiveness is a learned skill, one we have to practice. And that's good news! Because even if you're 80 years old, there is time to learn how to be assertive.

If your first reaction is "Look, I don't need lessons in how to be cold and mean-spirited," you really need this training. Most people do not understand the differences among the 4 styles of communication: assertive, passive, aggressive and passive-aggressive. The authors of *The Wellness Book* allowed me to use this wonderful wheel, which describes them all clearly. If you have ever heard people say that they

ASSERTIVE
communication reflects:

I count.
You count.

AGGRESSIVE
communication reflects:

I count.
You don't count.

PASSIVE AGGRESSIVE
communication reflects:

I count.
You don't count
but I'm not going
to tell you this.

PASSIVE
communication reflects:

I don't count.
You count.

get into trouble for being too assertive, I am here to tell you it isn't so. What they are getting into trouble for is being aggressive, not assertive. Who could be in trouble for communicating in a style that says "I count, and you count"? On the other hand, how could anyone respond positively to a style of communication that says "I count, and you don't!"

To help you get more comfortable with setting boundaries, being assertive, and saying "no," here is a terrific maxim: Separate the person from the request. Think about it. Why is it (honestly now) that we so often say yes, when we really want to say no? Isn't it usually because we're sure that the person we say no to will get upset, stop liking us, maybe even yell at us? And doesn't that sound an awful lot like third grade lunchroom thinking? When we can separate the person from the request, we can say no to the request without saying no to the person. That way we can say no without rejecting the person. If our worst fear comes true and our honesty is met with hurt feelings, anger or hostility, so what? Who'd want to be friends with someone who does not respect our honest need to set boundaries?

More Maxims:

- Assertive statements are honest. It is possible to look some one right in the eye, speak up...and lie! That is not being assertive. Express your feelings directly, openly, and above all honestly.
- Challenge yourself to put some time between a request and your response. "Let me check my calendar and get back to you," is a great way to say "maybe" and buy yourself the time you need to determine whether this is a time for saying no... or not.
- Assertiveness is not an all-or-nothing style of communication. We can be assertive with some people, passive with others, and aggressive with still others. Pamela Butler addresses this in her book *Self Assertion for Women*. I have included a chart she designed at the end of this chapter, which will help you determine what areas you need to work on...
- Pay attention to your body language. Make sure that the words you speak and the body language that goes with them match up. "Just let me check my calendar" while slouching out of the room conveys guilt.
- You have nothing to feel guilty for. Saying no is not a crime. "Just let me check my calendar" while standing tall and taking another bite out of your apple is much better.

- Being an effective communicator and an assertive person does not mean that you will always answer correctly, in control, without emotion. The need to be perfect is just another trap.
- Keep trying and keep practicing to replace old patterns with new, more effective ways of communicating.

Terrific Tips:
- Never automatically say 'yes' to a request. The answer may indeed BE yes, but put some time between the request and your response.
- Be gracious; thank the inviter for asking you.
- Say that you will get back to them at a specified, later time. Show them that they count by avoiding the nebulous "maybe" and be specific about when you'll respond.
- Decide whether you want to do it or not and if it's a time for boundaries, offer them another time or another service ... so long as it's really okay with you.
- Make a note and get back to the inviter with your decision.
- Remember to say "yes" to the person, even while you are saying "no" to the request.

Check list for assertiveness with different kinds of people.

The following checklist presents a number of people with whom we often have difficulty being assertive. Ask yourself how you would respond to each type of person. For example, the first item questions your ability to be assertive with strangers. Are you able to compliment a stranger (convey positive feelings)? If they are annoying you, can you express your annoyance (convey negative/protective feelings)? Are you able to refuse a request from a stranger who asks you to donate your time or money (can you set limits)? At a party, are you able to approach a stranger to talk (self-initiation)?

Rank each area using numbers on a scale from one (least difficult) to four (most difficult).

CATEGORY	POSITIVE FEELINGS	NEGATIVE FEELINGS	SETTING LIMITS	SELF INITIATION
STRANGERS				
PEOPLE IN AUTHORITY				
OPPOSITE SEX				
OLDER PEOPLE				
PEOPLE I WANT TO LIKE ME				
PEOPLE CLOSE TO ME				
PEOPLE I SUPERVISE				
MY SPOUSE/ PARTNER				
MY FATHER				
MY MOTHER				
TEENAGERS				
MY CHILDREN				
OTHERS				
TOTAL DIFFICULTY FACTOR				

After you complete the list, add up the total scores for positive feelings, negative feelings, limit setting and self-initiation. Which area has the highest score? Which has the lowest? Does it give you any ideas about your level of difficulty in being assertive with different kinds of people?

Ask yourself:
- What is not being assertive costing me?
- How would becoming assertive benefit me?
- What fears are keeping me from saying "no"? Are these fears realistic?
- Can I separate the person from the request? Can I separate myself from the response?

Chapter 13

Time Management

Time is like money. The less we have of it to spare,
the further we make it go.
~ Josh Billings

I am definitely going to take a course on time management...
just as soon as I can work it into my schedule.
~ Louis E. Boone

Time flies. It's up to you to be the navigator.
~ Robert Orben

Or so we wish. The truth is that most of us never learned how to manage time very well. They didn't have Time 101 when I was in school, and I'm betting they don't have it now. So, in the interest of time, here is the *Cliffs Notes* version.

Create a time log for one week. Simply keep track of everything you do in a day and how much time it takes you. Did I really spend two hours de-pilling my sweaters this week? Does my kitchen floor really

"Before we begin our Time Management Seminar,
did everyone get one of these 36-hour wrist watches?"

require that much attention? Did I spend an hour answering an email that could have been answered in two lines? Am I actually capable of spending half a day on the "net" seeing what the weather is like in Iceland right now?

Once you've completed your log, take a look at the following lists and answer the questions.

Time Bandits that are imposed on you:
- A ringing phone–Are you compulsive about answering the telephone? If you screened your calls, would they be less likely to interrupt you when you are engaged in a task?
- Unexpected visitors–Do you discourage or encourage unexpected visitors? When they do show up, can you be honest enough to tell them you can't visit just now?
- Deadlines–How well do plan for them? Do you wait until the last minute when anything could go wrong? Or do you give yourself enough time to do the job well?
- Assistants–Do you know how to delegate well?

Time Bandits that are self-imposed:
- Failure to delegate–Because of course no one can do it as well as you can. You'd be surprised by the number of people perfectly capable of taking some of your to-do list off your hands.
- Poor communication–When you do delegate, do you make sure you have communicated accurately and thoroughly?
- Bad attitude–Do you end up procrastinating, or spending too much time wallowing in resentment?
- Personal disorganization–Does finding the items you need to complete a task take longer than the task itself?

- Absent-mindedness—Do you have memory issues related to menopause, ADD, or just plain inability to focus? Ever find yourself striding purposefully into a room looking for something, and suddenly decide the spice cabinet needs to be alphabetized, or that your makeup drawer needs to be purged?

  - Lack of self-discipline—Do you often tell yourself you'll get to whatever it is right after you finish reading the paper, this article, this cup of coffee ...?
  - Superman/woman Syndrome—Do you insist that you can do it all, then find you can only do half?
  - Perfectionism—Do you do and then re-do a task because it just wasn't perfect the first time, or the second time, or...?

So what can we do?
  - Set priorities—What really needs to get accomplished <u>now?</u>
  - Schedule tasks for peak efficiency—Do you function better in the morning, afternoon, evening?
  - Allow time for interruptions
  - Budget enough time
  - Keep track of tasks that you put off and be willing to hire it out if need be. Can you hire a professional, college students, or trade tasks with a friend?

- Delegate—It really is possible that someone out there can actually do things well.
- Break down big tasks into smaller tasks. A wise man once said that the best way to eat an elephant is one bite at a time.

Your Time Bandits that are SELF-IMPOSED

_____
_____
_____
_____
_____
_____
_____
_____
_____
_____
_____
_____
_____
_____
_____
_____

Time Bandits that are IMPOSED ON YOU

_____
_____
_____
_____
_____
_____
_____
_____
_____
_____
_____
_____
_____
_____

DOMESTIC CHORES

How are duties divided in your home?
There should only be one marked in each row.

	Not Applicable	You	Person #2	Split 50/50	Hired Out	Other (Kids, etc.)
Grocery buying	——	——	——	——	——	——
Put food away	——	——	——	——	——	——
Doing the laundry	——	——	——	——	——	——
Ironing the clothes	——	——	——	——	——	——
Folding the clothes	——	——	——	——	——	——
Mow the lawn	——	——	——	——	——	——
Water the yard	——	——	——	——	——	——
Gardening	——	——	——	——	——	——
Trim the trees	——	——	——	——	——	——
Dust the furniture	——	——	——	——	——	——
Clean the bathroom	——	——	——	——	——	——
Clean the kitchen	——	——	——	——	——	——
Doing the dishes	——	——	——	——	——	——
Clean out dishwasher	——	——	——	——	——	——
Water house plants	——	——	——	——	——	——
Car Maintenence	——	——	——	——	——	——
Clean garage	——	——	——	——	——	——
Wash car	——	——	——	——	——	——
Polish car	——	——	——	——	——	——
Feed cat/dog	——	——	——	——	——	——
Wash cat/dog	——	——	——	——	——	——
Walk dog	——	——	——	——	——	——
Mop floor	——	——	——	——	——	——
Vacuum	——	——	——	——	——	——
Wash windows	——	——	——	——	——	——
Cook meals	——	——	——	——	——	——
BBQ	——	——	——	——	——	——
Pay bills	——	——	——	——	——	——

DOMESTIC CHORES

How are duties divided in your home?
There should only be one marked in each row.

	Not Applicable	You	Person #2	Split 50/50	Hired Out	Other (Kids, etc.)
Clean closets	——	——	——	——	——	——
Paint interior	——	——	——	——	——	——
Paint exterior	——	——	——	——	——	——
Take out garbage	——	——	——	——	——	——
Make beds	——	——	——	——	——	——
Change sheets	——	——	——	——	——	——
Sweep patio	——	——	——	——	——	——
Call service people	——	——	——	——	——	——
Change diapers	——	——	——	——	——	——
Other baby chores	——	——	——	——	——	——
Make lunches	——	——	——	——	——	——
Put kids to bed	——	——	——	——	——	——
Others:_____	——	——	——	——	——	——
_____	——	——	——	——	——	——
_____	——	——	——	——	——	——

Chapter 14

STRESS

Is everything as urgent as your stress would imply?
~ Carrie Latet

Stress is the trash of modern life. We all generate it but
if you don't dispose of it properly, it will pile up and overtake
your life.
~ Danzae Pace

If your teeth are clenched and your fists are clenched,
your lifespan is probably clenched.
~ Adabella Radici

I know, I know. Here it is...*again*. That lovely little catchword that "catches" the blame for so many ills and evils it has become cliché. Stress is blamed for everything from the common cold to cancer. Well, sit tight (or sit relaxed if you can), and get through this chapter. Because like it or not, stress has *earned* its terrible reputation. And a book about Wellness without stressing stress (pun intended) would be like a book about building without mentioning the tools.

Most people don't even know they are stressed until they take a class in stress management. Because so many of us spend so much of our lives in full distress, we've come to believe it's a normal state. It isn't. And just to prove it to you ...

- Stress is linked to the 6 leading causes of death–heart disease, cancer, lung ailments, accidents, cirrhosis of the liver, and suicide.

- About 90% of visits to primary care physicians are for stress-related problems.
- On an average workday, about a million employees are absent for stress-related problems.
- Over 40% of employee turnover is stress-related.
- 78% of Americans surveyed described their jobs as stressful & feel that work related pressure is steadily increasing.

Need I go on? Stress is the bad guy—bad for your health, bad for your happiness. So on the way to wellness, it will be important to arrest this particular villain.

If you've ever had the happy task of planning a wedding, you know that stress is not always caused by negative or unpleasant situations. Other examples of happy situations that are prime sources of stress are holidays, dinner parties, vacations, first dates, fund-raisers for good causes, even getting a haircut! How about going to the dentist, public speaking, or job interviews? I happen to love those last three things, but I'll bet they did not make your list of favorite things to do. I have a friend who loves the long drive home from work in Los Angeles (it takes her 45 minutes to drive 10 miles!), so she can think about her day and wind down. Wind down? I'm ready for a night in the psych ward ten minutes into L.A. traffic. Some people actually pay money to jump off a precipice and dangle at the bottom from a bungee cord. You couldn't pay me to do that. My sister, who is a flight nurse, wakes up from a dead sleep to an alarm tone, gets dressed in full flight gear, checks her helicopter, and is ready for take-off within 5 minutes...to a trauma! I'd still be feeling for my glasses. Some people handle stress better than others. Stress and beauty are both in the eyes of the beholder. You can decide what is stressful and what is not. It's kind of like choosing your battles.

"I learned about stress management from
my kids. Every night after work, I drink some
chocolate milk, eat sugary cereal straight
from the box, then run around the house in
my underwear squealing like a monkey."

Look over a typical day. When does the first stress response kick in?
Does it start when you bang your shin on the bed frame on your way
back from the bathroom; or when you look in the mirror and discover
a new mole (isn't that one of the seven warning signs of cancer?)
Does it happen when you kick the dog's water bowl over first thing
in the morning; or when you remember that your partner has an
appointment with the mortgage broker today? Does it stiffen your
upper back when you swing into the Starbuck's parking lot and find
it full just minutes before that 9 a.m. meeting? Does it drop your stomach down to your knees when you realize you left your notes on the
kitchen table; or give you the sweats when the clock says it's noon
and you're already five tasks behind? Maybe you love your job and
the stress doesn't get you until after 5 p.m. when you've got to show
up at the high school and try to explain why your son spray-painted
the gymnasium walls with "Bong Hits for Jesus." What stresses you
out? It helps to identify the big ones.

What are your most significant personal stressors?

1. _____

2. _____

3. _____

4. _____

5. _____

Most significant work stressors?

1. _____
2. _____
3. _____
4. _____
5. _____

Family stressors?

1. _____
2. _____
3. _____
4. _____
5. _____

Is there anything you can do to reduce these stressors? Some, perhaps not. Others you can change, often simply by communicating with the person causing the stress. It isn't a conflict if both people don't know about it. Give yourself permission to speak to your cubicle mate about the Van Halen CD he can't seem to work without. Maybe if you packed your own lunch you'd avoid the long lines and bad food at the Roach Coach or the Chinese place which are the only sources of sustenance near the office. Revisit the list and see if there are others you can change. That second look often reveals new ways to look at old stressors.

Maybe you suffer from chronic stress. The National Institute of Health defines chronic stress as ongoing worries that continue over several months or longer. *Chronic stress can shorten life expectancy by 15 - 20 years.* I volunteer with the National Alliance for the Mentally Ill. I speak to caregivers about stress. One elderly couple told me they have trouble sleeping and have had to install a dead-bolt on their bedroom door, since their schizophrenic grandson who lives with them has threatened to kill them. I cannot imagine living with this chronic stress. In fact, when my father was diagnosed with Alzheimer's, we discovered that family caregivers often die before the patient does.

Stress Reduction Techniques

All of the chapters in this "moving towards wellness" section can effectively be used as stress reduction techniques. A few caveats...give yourself time for mastery. I have students who say yeah, I tried to use deep breathing to fall asleep last night and it didn't work. It takes time to learn a technique. Second, even if you get pretty good at it, if it isn't something you enjoy, don't use it. I took a 16-week meditation class and finally got my mind to shut off, once I stopped laughing at the man snoring next to me. But it isn't really my thing. I would rather sit outside in my gazebo, listen to the birds chirping, and diaphragmatically breathe.

Other techniques not covered which I urge you to try - Yoga, Reiki, Visualization, Bio and Neuro feedback, Progressive Relaxation, Deep Breathing and any type of Exercise.

Experiment with them and keep the ones that work. I know someone who has a whole file folder marked simply Rx. It's her prescription folder for the techniques, reminders, and meditations that alleviate her stress. She also has a stack of five or six CD's with the same label: Rx – her musical prescription for relieving stress and anxiety. I keep a folder with smiley faces on it. I keep nice letters and cards, cartoons, jokes, all things that make me smile. Having a bad day? I can thumb through the file, smile and think yep, this person loves me, this one too.

Having a variety of techniques and devices will ensure that you'll have something to reach for in any situation. Not even the most proven technique can work every time for every situation. For example, while pulling on jogging shorts and shoes and running for a few miles can be very effective after a really hectic day of cerebral stress, it's not something you can do during a difficult conversation with your boss. And for goodness sake, don't set an unrealistic standard for yourself. Adding failure and guilt on top of stress makes any technique counter-productive!

The Relaxation and Stress Reduction workbook by Davis, Eshelman and McKay is an excellent resource. I like it for its comprehensiveness and because it gives you time for mastery. Some techniques you can learn quickly; some take awhile. One I really like is the *Thought Stopping Technique* combined with *Visualization*. It is so simple that most people I've suggested it to dismiss it without trying it. This technique involves concentration on unwanted thoughts, saying to yourself STOP to interrupt them, and then moving on to visualization. It is a good 3 a.m. technique when you wake up dwelling or obsessing on unwanted thoughts. I'm just saying, it works for me. And that's the key. It's all relative, and it's all subjective. But it's not optional! Find the ones that work for you and practice them.

There now. That wasn't so bad, was it?

WORKSHEET

MY MOST FREQUENT TROUBLESOME STRESS SYMPTOMS:

PHYSICAL - (examples: sweating, diarrhea, muscle tension, headaches, grinding teeth, more colds, stomachache, sleep disturbances, loss of sex drive, racing heart, indigestion)

1. _____
2. _____
3. _____

EMOTIONAL / PSYCHOLOGICAL - (examples: cannot concentrate, forgetful, irritable, crying, powerlessness, overwhelmed, panic, anxiety, loss of sense of humor, inability to relax)

1. _____
2. _____
3. _____

BEHAVIORAL - (examples: poor nutrition choices, excessive smoking, drinking, shopping, gum chewing)

1. _____
2. _____
3. _____

Your selected stress management techniques and steps to gain competence:

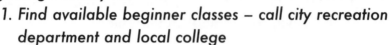

EXAMPLE:
A. *Take a yoga class twice a week beginning January 20*
1. *Find available beginner classes – call city recreation department and local college*
2. *Talk to Patty to see if she will take class with me*
3. *Get Jim to pick up kids from daycare on evenings of class*

Technique: _____
1. _____
2. _____
3. _____

Technique: _____
1. _____
2. _____
3. _____

Technique: _____
1. _____
2. _____
3. _____

Technique: _____
1. _____
2. _____
3. _____

Chapter 15

Sleep

No day is so bad it can't be fixed with a nap.
~ *Carrie Snow*

*A good laugh and a long sleep are the best cures
in the doctor's book.*
~ *Irish Proverb*

I can't go to sleep; Dreamland isn't open yet.
~ *Me when I was four*

There is a reason that sleep deprivation is used as a form of torture. Here is a short list of the effects that sleep deprivation causes: Aching muscles, inability to concentrate or focus, blurred vision, color blindness, suppression of the immune system, fainting, confusion, hand tremors, headaches, hypertension, impatience, irritability, memory lapse or loss, nausea, slurred speech, slow responses, increased risk of heart disease, and psychosis! Do I have your attention now, or didn't you get enough sleep last night?

People who sleep after learning and practicing a new task remember more about it the next day than people who stay up all night after learning the same thing. Ah, but college wouldn't have been college without those infamous all-nighters, would it?

Studies show that at least 40 million Americans suffer from over 70 different sleep disorders, and that 60 percent of adults report having sleep problems a few nights a week or more. Whoa!

And why? Well, I hate to blame that good old whipping boy for one more thing, but the fact is that Stress is the number one cause of short-term sleeping difficulties. The list of other reasons is as long as my arm and as varied as we are. Take my 5-year-old nephew for example. He told me he couldn't get to sleep at my house in California because he'd "forgotten" how to fall asleep here.

So let's not spend a lot of time discussing the psychodynamics of sleep disorders. Let's just figure out how to ensure that we get the 7 to 9 hours of sleep we need every night.

One of the most helpful insights about sleep came as a gift at a fancy hotel in Los Angeles. The management provides a "sleep kit" for their guests that includes a CD with soothing music, lavender spray, an eye mask, and ear plugs. My own experience that night is empirical evidence that these items really do work, and the research I conducted later would offer further scientific support that lavender, darkness, silence and music are effective sleep inducers.

I have my students in Santa Barbara to thank for this next one. What kind of sheets do I use? they asked. Surprised by this out-of-the-blue question, I scoffed at the relevance. They informed me that high-count Egyptian cotton sheets are heaven on earth to sleep in. When I joked with them that... "only in Santa Barbara..." they challenged me: Buy them, they said, and if "you don't love them, we will reimburse you." Some of you are nodding in agreement with them. You know that high-quality Egyptian cotton sheets are unparalleled for smoothness, softness, and some unmistakable quality that sets them apart. The rest of you can write and thank me later. And no, I won't be reimbursing you!

Alrighty then. You've got the lavender, some soft music, and great sheets. I ask you, what good will all that do if your bedroom is a mess? Let's leave the messy bedroom syndrome back in college with the all-nighters. Your bed is not the right recepticle for unfolded laundry, last month's newspapers, and a nearly empty box of Screaming Yellow Zonkers.

Your bedroom should be your oasis from stress. Keep it clean and picked up, cool and dark in the evenings. Overly bright lighting can be jarring. Add some medium lights that you can dim for a sweeter transition. Use a clip-on reading light to avoid the bright overheads that tell your brain it needs to stay awake.

Lights from the computer and other devices can be distracting. Cover them or turn them off. Turn your alarm clock away from the bed, that way it won't be inviting you to clock-watch if you wake up. And why set it on alarm? Is there a good reason to go from deep sleep to "fight or flight" at 6 a.m.? None that I can think of. Most alarm clocks have a music option. Or better yet, buy a fancy clock that uses a gradual increase in ambient light and peaceful sounds from nature, even aromatherapy, to awaken sleepers.

Develop a slowing down routine before you sleep. Mine includes a mist of lavender spray on my pillows and a few chapters from a good book. I keep a small tape recorder beside my bed in case I have a late night epiphany. Deep diaphragmatic breathing really helps me to get back to sleep if I'm awakened. The daily news often stresses me out, so I don't read it or watch it before bed. It always seems more palatable in the bright light of morning.

Regular exercise can help you fall asleep; many experts claim late afternoon workouts are best. Avoid workouts close to bedtime (one to two hours). They increase adrenaline and raise body temperature, which can keep you up.

If you haven't fallen asleep after 15 minutes, get out of bed and do something quiet, like reading. Or sip a glass of warm milk. Feeling stressed and anxious will only make it worse.

And finally:
- Don't drink or eat caffeine four to six hours before bed, and minimize your daytime use.
- Don't smoke, especially near bedtime or if you awaken in the night.
- Develop a regular bed time and go to bed at the same time each night.
- Don't watch TV in bed, or pay bills, or try to work.

Remember: when you don't make time to get enough sleep, it's a form of self-torture. Next time you catch yourself pulling an all-nighter, picture yourself willingly climbing onto a medieval rack, or inserting a thumbscrew into your own thumb. If that doesn't send you off to bed, you are definitely suffering from yet another symptom of sleep deprivation—denial!

WORKSHEET

List of changes you will make to improve your sleep habits:

1. _____
2. _____
3. _____
4. _____
5. _____
6. _____
7. _____
8. _____
9. _____
10. _____
11. _____
12. _____
13. _____
14. _____
15. _____
16. _____
17. _____
18. _____
19. _____
20. _____

SELF~ESTEEM

You cannot be lonely if you like the person you're alone with.
~ Dr. Wayne W. Dyer

Whatever good things we build, end up building us.
~ Jim Rohn

Low self-esteem is like driving through life with your hand-break on.
~ Maxwell Maltz

When you cannot get a compliment any other way...
pay yourself one.
~ Mark Twain

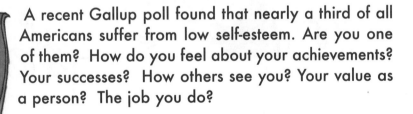

A recent Gallup poll found that nearly a third of all Americans suffer from low self-esteem. Are you one of them? How do you feel about your achievements? Your successes? How others see you? Your value as a person? The job you do?

Self-esteem is simply the opinion you hold of yourself, your self-acceptance rating. One of the hardest life lessons I've learned as an adult is that no matter how wonderful I think you are, if you don't believe it, I can't do anything about it. The longer I teach, the more frustrating this is. Self-esteem is about self-vali-dation. <u>You</u> have to believe you are wonderful.

Here's an exercise I've done with 6th grade students that's a sure-fire measure of their self-esteem. I ask them to draw their own favorite body part (I know,

95

this was risky). The two extremes were those who left the page blank (what did that say about their self-esteem?), and those who had trouble narrowing it down to just one! In between, were those who embellished the truth, drawing massive biceps (perhaps anticipating the future?) and those who depicted accurately their pretty blue eyes or their long legs.

How can there be such a discrepancy there? What factors influence a person's self-worth? Parents, friends, teachers, media? If you have parents who don't tell you you're wonderful, how do you cultivate healthy self-esteem? When our teenagers grow up watching television actresses wearing size 0 (when did that start?); 20-somethings who drive million-dollar cars; and American idols who can sing and dance like movie stars, do you think they feel pressured to measure up?

"Dan, you're my most valuable employee.
Your ineptitude consistently raises the
self-esteem of everyone you work with."

Often when a person is arrogant, we assume his or her self-esteem is through the roof, but as the Spanish proverb so aptly explains, "Tell me what you brag about and I'll tell you what you lack." I don't believe we should convey our self-confidence in a braggy, arrogant way. However, I do think it's okay to share with the world how fabulous we are. One of my students once wrote, "What would the world do without a jewel as precious as me?" She put a smiley-face next to the sentence, perhaps wanting to diminish her conceit. But you know what? She is a jewel. Tell it like it is, sister!

Try these strategies for improving your self-esteem:

◎ **Take risks.** Are you a risk taker? The kind who does not fear failure? The more willing you are to put yourself out there, the more you will strengthen your self-esteem. Isn't it wonderful when you take a risk and succeed? Whenever you take the risk, you are instantly successful, whether you turn into a professional ballroom dancer or not. The moment you decide to pursue a goal, you are successful.

It will be helpful to ask yourself what kinds of risks frighten you? Is it learning a new skill, activity, or hobby? Does the thought of moving paralyze you? Are you afraid to change careers? Would you talk to a stranger? Does changing your appearance, or going to a place you've never been before scare you?

List three fears that stop you from taking action:
1. _____
2. _____
3. _____

- What is the risk? What level of risk is it?
- What do you want the results to be?
- What fears do you have?
- What will you gain if you take this risk?
- What will you lose if you take this risk?
- Is there anything you can do to minimize your fears?

◎ **Avoid comparing yourself with others.** This is a deadly trap, and we all do it! This behavior does not, unfortunately, end with high school. Why not? Well, the media doesn't help. Television and movies are strong shapers of what we expect of ourselves, what we aspire to. Trouble is, hardly anyone can measure up to movie-star, super-hero standards. Americans enjoy seeing the failures and mishaps of others, especially celebrities. The folks who decide what we watch on television know that the "reality" shows that showcase the misfortunes, flaws, or mistakes of others make us feel better about ourselves. The best advice I can give you about developing healthy self-esteem is to stop comparing – to anyone. The only standard of measure should be yourself. Am I better today than I was yesterday? Did I learn something new this month? Am I healthier and happier ... did I help others more ... did I have more fun ... this week than I did last?

When you question yourself, your value, and self worth, you are undermining every gift you were ever given. It's like saying to the universe, "You didn't make me good enough, so I have to look out there for proof that I'm ok." Come on! If you believe you aren't good enough, you aren't. If you believe you are good enough, you are.

One of my students told me he lives by this statement: "If you think you can or if you think you can't, you're right." And since he shared this little maxim with us on the day he came to school dressed up as Elvis, I believe this guy is already a rock star!

◎ **Avoid putting yourself down.** Focus on your positive qualities. Who notices crow's feet when you have such killer eyes? What's a little extra weight when you've got such great legs? Stop frowning about your big feet, or fat knees, or crooked nose and focus on your snazzy sense of style, fabulous posture, or dancer's grace.

◎ **Accept compliments.** I compliment others all the time. No surprise to those who know me, I tell them just what I think, what I notice. I stop people every day to give them a genuine, specific compliment. And you know what? It makes *me* feel good. The other day I saw a young woman who looked familiar, and then I placed her. She'd been especially helpful to me whenever I shopped at the store she worked in. And I told her so. Her mother found me a few aisles later, and thanked me. She said I had no idea what that compliment had meant to her daughter. I stopped another woman in a restaurant recently to tell her I thought her outfit was happenin', that she should be in *Vogue* and she said, "Thank you. I am 89 years old." Eighty-nine and hot! We really can make someone's day and make our own in the bargain.

During a workshop I attended years ago, we did the following activity. One person sat center of circle and remain silent while everyone gave that person compliments. It was hard to stay silent and it made most people uncomfortable. What would that be like for you? Do you "dismiss" compliments with negative responses like "You're kidding! This old thing?" The inability to accept a compliment makes the complimentor feel silly for having brought it up at all. Just say "Thank you!" ... and mean it!

◎ **Approach challenges.** Remember our talk about taking risks? Don't shy away ...every attempt strengthens your self-esteem, and it's all about attitude. "I can do anything!" will get you a heck of a lot further than "But what if ..."

◎ **Associate with confident and successful people.** Ever notice how negative, unhappy people suck all the energy out of you? When you surround yourself with smart, accomplished, happy people, you soon realize you've stopped comparing because you're one of them.

◎ **Make and keep a list of past successes.** Maybe you were never class valedictorian, or the lead in your senior musical. Maybe you've never won the employee of the month or even a boxtop poetry contest. But there are dozens of things you have achieved. Save them, and savor them. A thank you note from a client, an appreciative comment from a co-worker, an I Love You Mom card from your child, or a "looking good" comment from a stranger (maybe it was me).

◎ **Set time aside each day for personal development.** Take an exercise class, learn to meditate, practice yoga, study Spanish. Or read great literature. A friend of mine took one whole summer to read the top 15 books of all time. By summer's end, he could discuss the power of

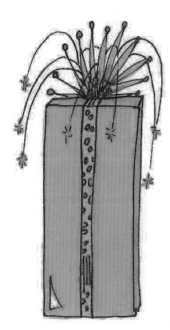

Tolstoy, the angst of F. Scott Fitzgerald, the bravado of Hemingway, the erotica of D.H. Lawrence. Another friend quit smoking and taught herself to knit. By the time she was over the pain of withdrawals, she had a gorgeous green and blue afghan. You decide. Self-improvement is a great way to feel better about you.

The reality is that we are all uniquely fabulous and abundantly talented. It's up to us to decide how much to cultivate, how much to share, how much to shine. Whenever I'm asked what my title is in the company I own, I tell them it's "Queen." And since I own a whole wardrobe of tiaras, it's tough to argue with me.

WORKSHEET

Things I love about me (I hope you wish there was more room here!)

_____   _____
_____   _____
_____   _____
_____   _____
_____   _____
_____   _____
_____   _____
_____   _____
_____   _____
_____   _____
_____   _____
_____   _____
_____   _____
_____   _____
_____   _____
_____   _____
_____   _____

Chapter 17

Pet Therapy

*A dog is the only thing on earth that will love you more
than you love yourself.*
~ Josh Billings

*There is no psychiatrist in the world like a puppy
licking your face.*
~ Ben Williams

*Animals are such agreeable friends – they ask no questions,
they pass no criticisms.*
~ George Elliot

My first pet ever was a tarantula. I know what you're thinking. But at four, it just didn't matter that the people staring at me while "Harry" crawled across my shoulders were horrified, not envious. Americans love animals. Dogs, cats and fish are the norm, but growing up with a herpetologist for a Dad, I appreciate spiders, snakes and lizards.

One of my favorite clients is the staff at the Santa Barbara Zoo. It is a great tribute to them that even with such happy, healthy employees, they continue to look for improvement. Innocence, playfulness, and unabashed caring abound in this wonderful environment; not very conducive to the chronically cranky. After my session, I wander the grounds, giggle at the antics of the otters, and stand in quiet reflection at the eerie resemblance of my brother-in-law to the apes. (Love you Rick!) Ever fed a giraffe? I defy you to look into those lavishly lashful eyes and feel those felt-covered lips on the palm of your hand without grinning.

I really believe that if everyone in the world had kittens, there would be no more war. This profundity came to me in my mother's living room, where a litter of Abyssinian kittens made up their minds to entertain us for the evening. They were so deliberately silly, it looked calculated, and we sat there watching them like we would watch TV. Okay, maybe kittens are not the key to world peace, but there is hard scientific evidence to support the fact that animals reduce stress, lower blood pressure, diminish depression, add years to life, even lower divorce rates.

"My therapy is quite simple: I wag my tail and lick your face until you feel good about yourself again."

Studies show that ...
- dog owners require less medical care for stress-induced aches and pains than do those who are dogless.
- heart attack victims who have pets live longer.
- watching a tank full of tropical fish lowers blood pressure, at least temporarily.
- of the 92 patients hospitalized in coronary care units for angina or heart attack, those who owned pets were more likely to be alive a year later than those who did not.

A ULCA study presented at the American Heart Association in 2005 was one of the first to document (and legitimize) that therapeutic dogs lower heart and lung pressure, anxiety, and stress in heart failure patients.

A University of Pennsylvania study demonstrated that watching fish eases stress and offers a means of treating hypertension.

In another study people spent the few minutes prior to undergoing oral surgery watching tropical fish in an aquarium. Their relaxation level was measured by their blood pressure, muscle tension, and behavior. Many dentist's offices now have fish tanks in the waiting rooms to ease the anxiety of waiting patients.

Psychosomatic Medicine reports that when people were given anxiety inducing tests, those with their dog or cat by their side were less stressed than those without.

Enough with the studies already! Spend some time with your pets, with your friends' pets, or at the zoo. But don't visit the shelters until you're ready. Adopting a pet is a wonderful thing, but returning the ones that "don't work" is heart-breaking.

Before you make a commitment, ask yourself ...

- Why do I want a pet?
- What will it need?
- What will it cost to care for it?
- What do I enjoy doing and will my new pet fit into that picture?
- Do I have adequate room and time for a pet?

_____

_____

_____

_____

_____

_____

_____

_____

_____

_____

_____

_____

- Check into pet certification programs and volunteer to bring your pet into a retirement home, or become a pet therapy volunteer at a local hospital.

And if you're just not a pet person, watch "Animal Planet." We'll make a convert out of you yet.

MusicTherapy

Music washes away from the soul the dust of everyday life.
~ Berthold Auerbach

Without music life would be a mistake.
~ Friedrich Wilhelm Nietzsche

Take a music bath once or twice a week for a few seasons.
You will find it is to the soul what a water bath is to the body.
~ Oliver Wendell Holmes

A sage and serene woman I know has a rich and varied selection of music in her CD collection. And there is one collection within her collection (you've heard of the play within the play?) marked Rx. For her, music is a prescription for whatever ails her. It is this small and select stack that she reaches for when she needs some serious therapy: when she's stressed, tired, in need of inspiration, and especially when she's in crisis. I thought she was nuts until my own "crisis" brought me to my knees one day and I tried it myself. Now I have my own Rx collection, and I know just where to find it – right between the Rolling Stones and Roxy Music.

Research has shown that music has a profound effect on our minds and bodies. Studies have discovered that...

- music activates the same parts of the brain that food and sex do. Oh really? Well, isn't that good news!

- whether you're playing it, composing it, or listening to it, it's all good. Heart rate, blood pressure, nervous system, you name it – they all benefit.

- according to music therapists, your favorite songs have therapeutic and recuperative powers.

- stroke victims use musical beats to learn to walk again.

- while monitoring seniors' blood pressure at regular intervals during a 10-week keyboard class, a boost in their immune systems was recorded.

Did you know that lullaby music can help premature babies in intensive care units to develop and flourish?

"It's a biological law that the heart will work to match any rhythm in the external environment. A slower heart rate, in turn, lowers your blood pressure and breathing rate—all of which will constitute a health-enhancing response," says Dr. Dharma Singh Khalsa. So when you are stressed, try music—just so long as it clicks along at about 60 beats per minute. I would hate to be responsible for a bunch of comatose bodies who tried to cure their stress with an ancient array of classical dirges.

Anxiety surveys and self-reports find that people listening to music show greatly increased feelings of relaxation and calmness. Other researchers have reported on the positive contribution of music to the effectiveness of biofeedback, guided imagery, and other established techniques. But don't wait for your next bout on the biofeedback bed ... Listen to music while doing anything!

Sound baths don't have to be particularly melodious. A British survey reports that 84% of people feel instantly relaxed when they are in nature; 42% preferred gazing at the sea, 33% picked a stroll in the park and 14% found calm by listening to birds singing.

Plan ahead. Pick a selection of soothing CD's for your car. They'll help prevent your next attack of "road rage."

And on a final note (no pun intended) in praise of the sound bath, here is a sweet little destination spot discovered by my friend Susan for the next time you're in the Palm Springs area.

The Integratron is an acoustically perfect tabernacle and energy machine sited on a powerful geomagnetic vortex in the magical Mojave Desert. Located in the tiny town of Landers, California, the entire building was constructed for the purpose of absorbing the positive energy of the geography while you indulge in the "sound bath" of your choice.

"The Integratron's parabolic shape, or sacred geometry, focuses and amplifies this energy, creating a space in which thousands of people have experienced energy beyond the normal visible/audible spectrum. Visitors who invest time inside the Integratron feel and experience energy, moving, rising, healing, and relaxing their frayed nerves and tired minds," says an excerpt from the website.

Its creator claimed the experience will add years to your life. Visit www.integratron.com for all the details. Now *where* did I put that old Jackson Browne album?

WORKSHEET

LIST FAVORITE MUSIC TO:

RELAX _____

ENERGIZE _____

WALLOW IN SELF PITY _____

FEEL ROMANTIC _____

DO HOUSEWORK _____

DANCE YOUR HAPPY DANCE _____

OTHER: _____

Chapter 19

Friendship

True friendship is like sound health; the value of it is seldom known until it is lost.
~ Charles Caleb Colton

No one is a failure if they have friends
~ The angel from It's a Wonderful Life

A friend is one who believes in you when you have ceased to believe in yourself.
~ Unknown

Years ago, a friend of mine gave me the best compliment ever. He called me his 3 a.m. friend. He said that no matter what time he called me, I was always there for him, even if it was 3 a.m. A simple statement with a huge impact. We have lots of friends and acquaintances in our lives, but who among them could you really call at 3 a.m. and get a warm reception? Make a list of the ones you could, and thank them. Just wait for a reasonable hour, okay?

One study shows that having a group of good friends around us may be more important to a long and healthy life than our families. (Those of you with "difficult" families are nodding your heads; I can see you.) Researchers found that people with the strongest network of good friends lived longer than those with just a few close friends.

I attended my Ethiopian class reunion a few years ago. It was an entire school reunion (the school was small) so we had students of all ages, including some of our teachers. Those bonds are just unbreakable, no matter how much time has passed. When I saw one of my best friends Jan from the sixth grade after so many years, I was jumping up and down like, well, like a 12-year-old. And just like those two inseparable 12-year-olds from that long-ago 6th grade class, we spent hours talking and giggling and whispering long into the night. It was as though we had never been apart.

I have a friend who is a hospital chaplain. She reminds me that when people are dying, it doesn't matter to them how much money they made, how many degrees they earned, how new their cars were, or even how clean they kept their living rooms. What they talk about are the people they love, and the times they spent with them. They don't regret the dust on top of the refrigerator, or the job they didn't go for. If they have regrets, they are for the hours they didn't spend or the words they didn't say to their loved ones. Are you making time for yours?

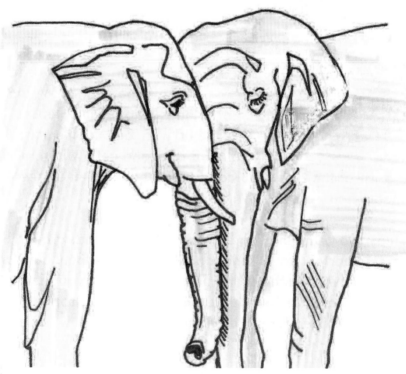

TIPS

E-mails are great, but nothing is better than getting together face-to-face. And when you can't see them, send cards (yes, the kind you actually mail), saying anything you want, but taking the time to say it!

Last year I started having "Fabulous Women" parties. I make crowns for each one–foam ones from the craft stores with rhinestones and their names pasted on. Most of them don't know each other before-hand, but there is something about that glittering tiara that bonds them. They always click and it is always fun. I just love to introduce my wonderful friends to each other this way. My newest party is a "People I Love Party," urging people to wear whatever they have in their closet that they love and haven't worn for a long time, glitter and boas encouraged (although, hello, who doesn't wear those all the time?).

How about a gathering where each invitee is asked to bring some-one the others don't know?

You could start a book club, a writers' group, or a craft party (invite a crafter to attend and give lessons). You could have a cake deco-rating or a scrapbooking party. A friend of mine has a Christmas gift-wrapping party; another has a Christmas cookie-baking fest. A teacher friend has a word-searching party to help her develop read-ing curriculum for the coming year. And hey, there's no better way to get that kitchen painted or that yard bricked over than to have a party around it!

113

WORKSHEET

1. What kind of parties could you have?   Who could you invite?

_____

_____

_____

_____

_____

_____

_____

_____

2. 3 A.M. FRIENDS LIST Whom do you consider a friend who would be there for you, no questions asked anytime you need them?

_____

_____

_____

_____

_____

_____

_____

Chapter 20

Aromatherapy

My nose loves to smell brownies.
~ Emily, age 6

Smell is a potent wizard that transports us across thousands of miles and all the years we have lived. The odors of fruits waft me to my southern home, to my childhood frolics in the peach orchard. Other odors, instantaneous and fleeting, cause my heart to dilate joyously or contract with remembered grief. Even as I think of smells, my nose is full of scents that start awake sweet memories of summers gone and ripening fields far away.
~ Helen Keller

I'm happy when my little brother doesn't stink.
~ Delaney, age 6

In the classic cult movie *Harold and Maude*, Ruth Gordon's character owns an early pred-ecessor to today's aromatherapy. Her odoriffic machine, she declares, " ... gives the nose a treat, a banquet for the olfactory" complete with the smell of old books, newly mown grass and snowfall on 42nd street.

The wisdom of Helen Keller, six-year-old sages, and the eccentric 79-year-old Maude notwithstanding, can this airy fairy new age idea really work? Oh ye of little faith. Check out the following:

Aromatherapy is now being used in medical facilities – not as an "alternative" therapy – but as a proven complement to the treatment plan. Research has found that ...

- the scent of peppermint allowed participants in an exercise study to work out longer and harder than those who did not smell peppermint
- when patients undergoing an MRI smelled vanilla essential oil, their anxiety dropped 63%
- a drop of strawberry essential oil calms patients prior to surgery
- elderly patients slept "like babies" when a lavender aroma was wafted into their bedrooms at night. These patients had complained of difficulty falling asleep and had to take sleeping pills prior to the aromatherapy
- peppermint and jasmine help beat the blahs
- pumping essential oil into an area where keyboard entry operators worked, it was discovered that when exposed to lavender, errors dropped 20%, jasmine 33% and lemon an amazing 54%!
- when exposing test subjects to the scent of peppermint during an exam, those who were exposed scored 20% higher than those who were not

Consider this. The Denver Zoo is now experimenting with aromatherapy for animals. If smells can tame tigers, who are we to argue with that?

While the experts can't seem to agree about why aromatherapy works, they do agree that it does. Evidence suggests that scents affect the limbic system—the part of our brain that controls moods, emotions, and memory. Aromas affect heart rate, blood pressure, muscle tension and skin temperature; and the changes can be scientifically measured.

Not convinced? Well, here's a real-life story about the healing power of smells.

One of my college students, Dawn, chose aromatherapy as a topic for our class presentation. She began by disclosing her own experience with an alcoholic treatment program. Dawn knew she needed help and had promised her family she'd go, but was distraught over leaving her two young sons. The week before she entered the inpatient facility, she bought a new baby blanket and a stuffed dog she named Sobriety. One of her sons got the blanket, the other "Sobriety" to sleep with for a week. Dawn took them with her to treatment, and that first night in bed, she wrapped the blanket around her shoulders and hugged "Sobriety" to her face. Enveloped by the scents of her two little boys, Dawn fell asleep easily and slept soundly for the duration of her treatment.

HOW TO:

Find a good aromatherapy store (that $2 scented candle at Econo-Drug or a couple of commercial plug-ins do not qualify as essential oil). Experiment with the samples, talk to the nice lady behind the counter. And trust your responses to what you are smelling. If cranberry makes you cringe, or musk oil makes you manic, leave them alone.

Have some goals in mind (to feel calmer, to energize in the afternoon, to stimulate creative juices) and take several scents home to try.

Here are some suggested uses—the key word here being "suggested."

- Use a sprayer with a mixture of oil and distilled water. I use peppermint oil and pass it around my classes in the afternoon when students are getting sleepy.

- Heat the oil in a diffuser for use in your office or bedroom.

- Try putting peppermint oil on a towel around your neck. Treadmill? What treadmill?

- Mix some oil with unscented lotion and rub it on your wrists, temple, or neck.

- Put several drops of essential oil on the shower wall where the spray hits, and let the steam diffuse the scent.

- Spray lavender scent on your pillow before you get into bed

And breathe...

Chapter 21

Vacation

Vacation used to be a luxury, but in today's world it has become a necessity.
~ Author Unknown

A vacation is what you take when you can no longer take what you've been taking.
~ Earl Wilson

I cannot believe that I am writing a whole chapter designed to convince you to take vacations. It feels like I'm trying to convince a starving man to eat. So, I will let these statistics and true stories speak for themselves.

- One in five Americans show up at work if ill or injured.
- 31 percent of U.S. workers don't always take all of their vacation days, yet ...
- 93 percent of Americans believe that regular vacations increase productivity and relieve stress.
- Americans give back an average of three vacation days each year.
- The value of the vacation days that Americans are projected to give back this year alone is estimated at almost $54 billion.
- More than half of American vacationers use email or cell phones to monitor work issues while away from the office.
- Men who take vacations every year reduce their overall risk of death by about 20 percent, and their risk of death from heart disease by as much as 30 percent.

- A computer tech guy at a local hospital returned from his lunch hour dressed in such bloody clothes, he was mistaken for an ER doctor. He had fallen, hit his head, splashed some water on his face to clean up, and returned to work.
- A young family traveled to Disney World for their annual vacation. Both parents worked outside the home; they had two young children. Upon their late arrival in a Florida hotel room, the whole family was exhausted and headed for bed. But not before Dad had set the alarm for 6 a.m. He wanted to be first in line for Disney World the next morning. (Ok, this was my sister and her family.)

"We also have some part-time positions available for people who only want to work 60 or 80 hours a week."

I just have one question: What is the matter with you people? Excuses run the gamut. You'd rather get money back for your unused days; planning ahead is too much of a hassle; you just can't get away. Well, here's a hint: Many employers consider it a red flag when workers never take their vacations.

Taking vacations is more than just a frivolous pleasure – it may actually be good for your health. In his outstanding book, *Chained to the Desk*, Bryan Robinson cites the problems resulting from workaholism: inability to enjoy leisure activities, exhaustion, stress, and an increase in relationship problems with family members and co-workers.

Go on vacation. And if you're one of the many vacationally challenged, here are some sure-fire ways to get the most out of your time away.

TIPS:

1. *Take short trips frequently.* I have a friend who had to take 9 vacation days in 2 months, or she'd lose them. So she decided to take 9 Wednesdays off in a row. For nine blissful weeks, she worked 2 days, took a day off, worked 2 more and then enjoyed her weekends. Or take advantage of those fabulous 3-day weekend getaways offered by spas and hotels to locals in your area. That way you don't spend all your precious time and money getting there.

2. *Cut the cord.* Sever all ties to the office. They can survive without you. Who knows, perhaps a vacation for you, is a vacation *from* you for your co-workers.

3. *Savor the memories.* Keep a journal or make a scrapbook of the trip – something you can reflect back on, savor, and share. Bring a token reminder such as a picture, shell, or souvenir to the office so you can glance at it each day and smile. One of my students Tony took this picture while basking in the sun in the Caribbean. He uses it as a screensaver.

4. *Leave a buffer when you return.* Nothing will make you feel worse about going back to work than the last-minute rush. As in: your plane arrives home in the middle of the night. You report to work the next day exhausted, put in a full first day back, and then return home to open suitcases, dirty clothes, and a very bad attitude. Plan a day or two to unwind when you get home before returning to work.

5. *Recognize that vacations can't cure burnout.* A weekend, even a month of vacation can't cure burnout, or make a dreadful job wonderful or even tolerable. What it will do is give you the perspective you need to either approach your job differently, or find another one.

6. *Make a list of the things you would love to see or do...* then do it! My friend Starr sent an e-mail challenging her friends to make a list of the things we want to do in our lives before we die. To inspire us, she made her list and shared it, and she continually adds to it. Shortly after the email went out, Starr went to dance camp in Vegas, had a fantastic time, and is planning to quit her job to teach salsa dancing. (Okay, I made up that last part.) The point is that Starr is crossing things off her list, loving her life, and her job. Don't just dream it, do it.

WORKSHEET

I HAVE ALWAYS WANTED TO SEE ... I HAVE ALWAYS WANTED TO GO ... I HAVE ALWAYS WANTED TO DO ...

_____
_____
_____
_____
_____
_____
_____
_____
_____
_____
_____
_____
_____
_____
_____
_____
_____
_____
_____
_____
_____
_____
_____
_____

Chapter 22

Volunteerism

The fragrance remains on the hand that gives the rose.
~ *Unknown*

What do we live for, if it is not to make life less difficult for each other?
~ *George Eliot*

Great opportunities to help others seldom come, but small ones surround us daily.
~ *Sally Koch*

I once asked a wealthy acquaintance what he did to give back to society. His answer? "I pay my taxes." He could tell by my look that I was shocked. "Well what *could* I do?" he asked defensively.

Perhaps it was Africa; or maybe it was my parents; more likely both. But somehow I have always understood the importance of giving back. What I wanted to tell this guy was that he qualifies for just about any volunteer position he could name. He qualifies because the number one requirement in most non-profits is the ability to draw breath. They would be thrilled to have him! Whether it's stuffing envelopes or driving the disabled to their jobsites – they would put him to work. Shoot, he doesn't even need an imagination! Just willingness.

We complain so much more than we should. We whine when it rains; we grouse when the coffee machine is broken; we snivel when gas prices go up ... again. But when we work with people who have leaky roofs, who can't afford coffee, much less a car – our perspective shifts. And suddenly, the snag in our new cashmere sweater doesn't seem like such a tragedy after all.

The many benefits of volunteering:

- Improves mood and self esteem. Face-to-face helping gives us a "Helpers High."
- Reduces excessive self-centeredness. (It is *not* all about you, all the time.)
- Reduces social isolation. You meet new and like-minded people. I met many of my closest friends while volunteering.
- Helps with depression and anxiety.
- Improves your social support network while increasing the level of community wellness.
- Helps you develop confidence in your own abilities. (You *can* make a difference!)
- Teaches us a variety of new skills.
- Enhances your résumé.

I gain perspective on my own life whenever I volunteer. Working with people who aren't as lucky as I am instantly transforms my attitude. How can I possibly stay depressed about needing to buy a new garbage disposal when I'm working with people on food stamps? And the fact that my allergies are flaring up again seems so un-important when I've just spent time with someone on Hospice!

Having spent many years working in non-profits, I am here to tell you that we feel like getting out the party hats when people offer to help. And here's the really cool thing: the party actually happens! I had a group of retired seniors who helped me stuff packets one week for a fund-raiser. They chatted, laughed, made new friends, and left feeling great about themselves. When was the last party you went to that gave you all that?
AND SPEAKING OF PARTIES...

Every year I have a holiday party. What I always end up with are fabulous memories ... and way too many unopened bottles of wine that guests had brought as hostess gifts. So I decided to change that. Now when I send out my invitations, I choose a charity and enclose an article about it. I ask people to bring something that will support that charity to the party ... like unwrapped new toys, for example. This year, one of my students suggested giving backpacks to children who are taken out of a domestically violent home. The backpacks are filled with new pajamas, soap and toothpaste, and a small stuffed animal. We made a big difference that year in the lives of some sad, scared kids; and I didn't have to figure out how to drink 50 bottles of wine all by myself! A friend liked the idea so much that he did the same thing for a party he gave a few months later. That's the beauty of it. If it's true that violence begets violence, then surely we are proving that love begets more love.

WORKSHEET

CAUSES THAT ARE NEAR AND DEAR TO YOUR HEART:

1._____
2._____
3._____
4._____
5._____

ISSUES THAT HAVE TOUCHED YOU:

1._____
2._____
3._____
4._____
5._____

AREAS WHERE YOU EXCEL:

1._____
2._____
3._____
4._____
5._____

AREAS THAT YOU ARE NOT COMFORTABLE WITH:

1._____
2._____
3._____
4._____
5._____

Chapter 23

Simple Pleasures

*A truly happy person is one who can enjoy the scenery
on a detour.*
~ Unknown

Simple pleasures are life's greatest treasures.
~ Unknown

In her book, *Simple Abundance*, Sarah Ban Breathnach says that some days are shaped by simple pleasures, and others are redeemed by them. She then goes on to describe a perfect summer day filled with all her simple pleasures – "… roaming in interesting shops, irresistible reading, an ice cream cone for lunch, strolling the boardwalk, cooking dinner with a good friend, a refreshing outdoor shower …"

Knowing what brings us pleasure – every time – can redeem a not-so-perfect day as well. You know, the days when the auto shop calls to tell you they'll have to keep your car another week; or the job promotion went to someone else; or your best friend decides to move away. That's when deliberately seeking out your simple pleasures will be most important. Maybe you hate roaming those stupid little shops, maybe you'd rather see a movie than read, or eat great cheese instead of ice cream. Maybe you can't cook a lick, and a bubble bath has more appeal than a primitive outdoor shower. Do you know what you really love?

Take time with this short little chapter. It's one you'll come back to often.

"Imagine a world without pleasure. Life would appear colorless and humorless. A baby's smile would go unappreciated. Foods would be tasteless. The beauty of a Bach concerto would fall on deaf ears." So begins the book *Healthy Pleasures*. We've all heard these oft-repeated quotes asking us to "Stop and smell the roses" and reminding us that "The best things in life are free." But how often do we really notice the little things that make us smile?

This chapter could be called "Life's Simple Pleasures According to _____ (you)." And toward that end, there is a nifty page with lots of lines on it (I've included lots of these in this book because the truth is that one of my simple pleasures is a book I can write in!) Use this one to list the things guaranteed to calm you, make you laugh, or take you "somewhere else."

"Howl at an ambulance or fire siren every chance you get.
Run around the room in circles with a sock in your mouth.
Eat a messy meal without using your hands or utensils.
Ask a friend to scratch your belly..."

My neice Madison filled one out when she was eight and she had a wonderful list, including hot chocolate and whipped cream. I'm going to bet that even though she's a teenager now, that list has stuff on it she still loves.

I suggest that people in the workplace fill out this list and then share them with co-workers. They are great to have on file when you want to treat someone.

Can't get started? Well, here are some of mine: reading greeting cards in the store; hearing my favorite song on the radio; no lines at the grocery store; hot chocolate with whipped cream (thanks Maddie!); waking up early when you realize you don't have to; watching animals in a pet store or zoo or even at home; drinking milk out of a champagne glass; a clean car (rare but nice); watching birds at my feeders; kids laughing. All free, and all fabulous.

And here's another list (my editor said I could use hers): A truly great cup of freshly ground coffee; the sun at my back on a country walk; any song by Louis "Satchmo" Armstrong; clean sheets; a John D. McDonald mystery; nosing my cat; painting my toenails a new color; the poems of W.B. Yeats; making homemade soup; going to a midnight movie all by myself with a Rice Krispie Treat in my purse.

Okay, come on now ... this should be EASY!

My Simple Pleasures

Chapter 24

Moving Right Along

Wellness, like paradise, is not a destination at which we ever fully arrive. It is elusive and there is always room for improvement. One simple guideline to fall back on whenever we forget what we are striving for and why, is contained in a quote from none other than Albert Einstein's wife. A reporter once asked her if she understood relativity, to which she replied "Oh, no! It is not necessary to my happiness." Right on, Mrs. Einstein.

As we continue our journey toward Wellness, it seems especially fitting to end this book (especially since it has "wild" in its title) with the Native American parable, *The Two Wolves*.

I love this story because it brings us right back to the fundamental theme of the work we've been doing here: that it's all about the choices we make. See if you don't agree.

The Two Wolves

A grandfather and grandson were walking through the forest one winter evening. From far away, they heard the wolves howl.

"Hungry wolves!" said the grandson.

"Yes, just like the ones inside us," said the grandfather.

"What do you mean? We have wolves inside us, hungry wolves?"

"Yes, we do. Two wolves."

"Two wolves?"

"One wolf is always angry and resentful, greedy, full of false pride, self-pity and arrogance. He bears his teeth and is always ready to pounce."

"And the other one?"

"The other one has it in him to be a great pack leader. He protects the young and knows where to take the pack when the winds get too fierce. He is full of love, hope, kindness, joy, compassion, serenity and generosity. He is peaceful and humble and has a great sense of humour."

"What do these two wolves do inside of us?"

"They fight with each other for your soul."

"And which one wins, grandfather?"

"The one who wins, my grandson, is the one you feed."

Thank you for letting me into your lives, even for just the time it took to read this story. It is one of my greatest joys to impart what I have learned. - Jean Steel

About the Author

Born in L.A. and raised in Africa and Asia, Jean Steel's unique life perspective has been healing sick companies, and inspiring individuals for over 20 years. Moving frequently and changing schools often, she developed strength, resilience, flexibility and a keen appreciation for life.

Jean graduated from the University of California at Santa Barbara with a degree in Sociology, and then worked for ten years as a health educator in a drug and alcohol center. In Sacramento, California, she designed a preventative medicine program for Kaiser Permanente.

Jean earned her Master's Degree from Sacramento State in Mind & Body Health and Wellness, a program she designed herself.

With a long and prestigious list of clients that includes hospitals, universities, cities, and internationally known corporations, Steel's work has had a major impact on the productivity and quality of work delivered, and has enriched the working lives of countless corporate staff. Her talks have also inspired small businesses and individuals working in difficult, stressful environments.

Self-responsibility, the power of choice, and the art of mindfulness are a few of the themes guiding her powerful, interactive talks and seminars. Humor is a hallmark, and no one delivers a story with more down-home hilarity than Jean Steel.

About the Illustrator

Illustrator Suz Steel Roehl, is Jean's middle sister. A flight nurse by trade for CALSTAR – California Shock Trauma Air Rescue – she also competes in 3-day cross country events (riding one of her three horses), and follows her passions for gardening, traveling, hiking, and making a mean margarita. She lives with her husband Rick and her two sons Alec and Tony on the Central Coast of California.

Notes